Introduction
to
Linear Programming

Introduction
to
Linear Programming

R. STANSBURY STOCKTON
Chairman
Department of Production Management
Indiana University

1971

RICHARD D. IRWIN, INC. Homewood, Illinois 60430

Irwin-Dorsey Limited, Georgetown, Ontario

First Printing, March, 1971

Second Printing, October, 1971

Library of Congress Catalog Card No. 77–146728

PRINTED IN THE UNITED STATES OF AMERICA

Preface

Ten years ago linear programming was still relatively new as an academic subject and relatively untried in American business. Today the many methods of management science are well established both in school-of-business curricula and in the analysis of complex management problems in industry around the world. In this sense the relevance of these techniques to the education of current and future business executives has been widely accepted.

Linear programming is a logical first technique for the beginning student of quantitative methods because of its limited mathematical complexity. Since there is much to be taught in introductory courses, one would like to accomplish this learning result with a minimum expenditure of classroom time. Given this time constraint, the critical question today is pedagogical. How can large numbers of students, at least some of whom have limited aptitudes and backgrounds, learn basic programming methods most effectively? This book is designed to meet the need for suitable materials in dealing with this problem.

The objective of this book is to introduce students to linear programming methods within the broader context of management decision making. While the mathematics is treated in some detail, every effort has been made to explain these methods in terms and contexts which should be familiar to the typical student of business administration. This approach assumes that a basic understanding of the computational routines is necessary to utilize linear programming as either an analyst or as a decision maker.

Three features have been incorporated in the preparation of this text. First, the chapters on the graphical and simplex methods have been written so that the various steps in the routines are clearly identified and related to one another. Second, a portion of each chapter is devoted to interpretation and implementation of optimal solutions. Experience has shown that this is one point in the decision process where communication between analyst and decision maker can break down.

The third and major new feature of this book is the incorporation of self-checking questions and problems at the end of each key section. These materials give the reader an opportunity to test his comprehension of each step in the computational routines before proceeding to more advanced sections. It is our hope that this "self-teaching" feature will help to improve the effectiveness of both the student's and his instructor's efforts. Proper use of these materials should enable the reader to discover and to clarify his individual questions as they arise and to progress at his own speed. Fewer questions from students about technical details should enable the instructor to utilize classroom time for discussion of the managerial implications of linear programming and/ or other quantitative methods of analysis.

Like any author, I am indebted to many people for their cooperation in making this book possible. My colleague, Professor Michael F. Pohlen, has been especially helpful in making suggestions and in commenting on possible improvements in early drafts. Additional suggestions and much help on the problems have been provided by my graduate assistant, Mr. Andrew Weisman. Finally, I am indebted to Mrs. Carol Jones who typed the final manuscript.

February, 1971   R. STANSBURY STOCKTON

Contents

4 The Simplex Method   46

5 The Transportation Method   82

1 Linear Programming and the Decision Process

1.1 THE MANAGER AND LINEAR PROGRAMMING

Linear programming is one of a number of recently developed analytical techniques that have proved useful in solving certain types of business problems. These quantitative methods of problem solving, like many employed widely in industry today, are based upon mathematical and statistical concepts. Therefore, they present a problem to the business executive who finds it difficult to translate what appears to be mathematical "jibberish" into meaningful terms. Under such circumstances, the businessman tends to equate his inability to understand with impracticality and, as a consequence, to dismiss these new techniques as a plot by mathematicians to confuse and befuddle businessmen! There is evidently some truth in the adage that "people would rather live with problems which they cannot solve than with solutions to those problems which they cannot understand."

Publications in the field of management science contain a large number and variety of business applications of these ana-

1

lytical methods, including linear programming. Furthermore, the number and scope of these applications can be expected to increase in the future as variations and refinements in the methods are developed. Tomorrow's business executives will clearly need to be familiar with these methods and capable of applying them to complex problems within their organization.

Much of the credit for demonstrating the applicability of linear programming methods to business problems belongs to those people engaged in operations research. However, it is not necessary to be in systems analysis to learn the fundamentals of the subject. In fact, lack of understanding on the part of line managers appears to be a major factor limiting both present and future applications of many potentially useful explicit methods of analysis.

Inasmuch as linear programming represents a type of "model," one appropriate method of study would be to place it within the broader framework of the managerial decision-making process. Most statements of the latter are adaptations of the so-called scientific method. One of the justifications for the study of any quantitative method of analysis is that these methods illustrate all steps or phases of the decision-making process on an explicit basis. We assume that the discipline skills developed through the use of explicit exercises will be applicable to other problems, including those in which many factors are essentially qualitative.

A second reason for studying linear programming is that a general "administrative" understanding of the method is a necessary prerequisite of effective use of the technique within any organization. Line managers—as differentiated from staff specialists or analysts—play an important role in the initial and final stages of problem-solving projects, that is, in the formulation of the problem and in the evaluation and application of the findings. They must, as a consequence, be capable of effective communication with any staff specialist, including the operations or systems analyst. A more specific objective in the study of linear programming might therefore be stated as the development of sufficient insight into the method to enable one to (1) recognize problems that might be subjected to analysis by the method, (2) assist the analyst in the initial stage of the investigation, (3) evaluate and interpret the results intelligently, and (4) apply the results with the confidence that comes only with some understanding of the "whys" as well as the "whats" involved.

1.2 AREAS OF APPLICATION

Linear programming methods may chiefly be applied to the general class of problems known as *allocation problems*. Economists have traditionally defined such problems as those involving the allocation of scarce resources among alternative ends according to some criterion. Scarce resources for the business firm include capital, personnel, equipment, and materials. The various products and/or services that constitute the output of the firm represent alternative ends to which resources must be allocated. The criterion or objective, on the basis of which allocation decisions are to be made, may be some form of profit maximization or any other appropriate measure of desired performance.

Business managers always have been and always will be confronted with allocation decisions. The methods of analysis used to resolve these problems can and should be varied. For example, decisions based upon judgment and intuition may be satisfactory where the number of factors in the problem is limited and their relationships are clear. More difficult problems may require preliminary data collection, followed by the application of some formal method of analysis such as those characteristic of industrial engineering. The adequacy of these standard techniques falls off rapidly, however, as the number of variables in the problem increases. Linear programming is most appropriate for complex allocation problems that cannot be handled satisfactorily with conventional analytical techniques.

Many types of allocation problems are found in business, especially in the production or operations function. Some examples to which linear programming methods have been successfully applied are:

DETERMINATION OF PRODUCT MIX.   The types and quantities of products to be manufactured during the next planning period must be determined. The relative profitability of the items in the product line varies. The planned product mix must take into consideration expected demand, the capability and capacities of production and distribution facilities, and management policies, such as policy on products carried to "round out the line." Given these limitations or restrictions on the mix, the solution should also make maximum economic sense; that is, it should maximize profits.

BLENDING OR MIXING PROBLEMS.   One or more products are manufactured by mixing or blending various ingredients, for example, paint, cattle feed, and petroleum products. Many different combinations of these ingredients can result in end products that will meet all technical specifications. Given the availability and relative costs of the ingredients, which blend will result in minimum material cost per unit of end product?

PRODUCTION SCHEDULING AND INVENTORY PLANNING. Given a seasonal demand and limited production facilities, what production schedule and planned inventory levels over the next planning period will meet expected demand and also result in minimum cost?

MACHINE LOADING.   A series of orders is to be processed through a group of machines. The cost of processing each order depends in part on the particular machine to which it is assigned. Limited machine capacity precludes assignment of each order to the lowest-cost equipment. What allocations of available capacity to the series of orders will result in minimum total processing cost?

SHIPPING AND PHYSICAL DISTRIBUTION PROBLEMS.   Goods are to be shipped from several production facilities having limited capacities to field warehouses that anticipate a given demand over the next planning period. Transportation and/or production costs vary among the alternative methods of supplying the warehouses. What physical distribution pattern will be both within the capacity and demand restrictions and will at the same time minimize total production and distribution costs over the planning period?

1.3 BASIC ASSUMPTIONS

All explicit analytical methods are based upon certain assumptions. Just as one must understand certain accounting conventions to use accounting statements intelligently, one must understand the basic assumption of any quantitative analytical tool if it is to be applied properly. The two central assumptions in all linear programming methods are (1) *linearity* and (2) *certainty*. *Linearity* means that all problem relationships can be expressed in the form of linear equations. The straight-line method of depreciation assumes that capital value decreases at a linear rate. Break-even charts assume that both variable costs and revenue are linear functions, that is, that they increase in direct proportion to output. The term *certainty* indicates that no significant variations are expected in the numerical value for a problem factor. Average cost, for example, may be used in making a decision even though actual cost may vary slightly from this average. Statistical quality control, on the other hand, is based upon the expected variations in a process within the control limits, i.e., a degree of uncertainty exists. Linear programming is an appropriate analytical tool only for those complex allocation problems that are characterized by both linearity and certainty.

An understanding of linear functions is so fundamental to understanding linear programming that Chapter 2 is devoted to a general review of this subject. The exact meaning and significance of linearity and certainty in a programming context will become apparent in the explanations of the various methods. It should be noted that, by reducing the mathematical complexity of the methods, these assumptions make linear programming a good starting point for the beginning student of quantitative methods of analysis. The ultimate payoff, of course, is in solving real problems. The usefulness of linear programming, like that of any other method of analysis, is dependent in large part on the reasonableness of the assumptions about the problem being studied.

1.4 LINEAR PROGRAMMING METHODS

The mathematical computational procedures of linear programming depend in part on which of the several programming methods is adopted for a particular problem. The basic or general case is called the *Simplex* method, since it is based upon the simplex algorithm. Certain types of allocation problems may be solved by special, less complex, versions of the Simplex method, known as the Graphical and Transportation methods. In addition there are a number of variations, such as the so-called Index method which yields only approximate solutions but has minimum computational requirements. All methods are, in essence, nothing more than effective search procedures that seek optimal solutions to allocation problems in which there are more unknowns than linear equations. In this sense, linear programming may be viewed as systematic trial and error in which the most promising shortcuts to a solution are indicated by mathematics rather than by intuition and elbow grease.

1.5 COMPUTERS AND LINEAR PROGRAMMING

Formulating a business problem for solution by any linear programming method requires setting up a large number of linear equations. Once the problem is framed, an initial solution is determined. A set of operating rules is then applied to determine whether a better solution exists and, if so, to develop an improved solution. The solution process is iterative; that is, the rules are applied again and again until such time as an optimal solution is found.

The fact that the computational rules and procedures for linear programming are so well defined makes this a natural application for modern electronic computers. Standard programs are available for linear programming on nearly all computer hardware today, so that the burdensome task of computer programming is less of an obstacle than in earlier years. Problems of limited complexity, like those included in subsequent chapters, may be solved efficiently on paper. However, as the number of variables in the problem increases, the magnitude of the computational task increases sharply. For this reason the use of expensive computer time can be justified in the analysis of most complex business problems.

2 Review of Linear Functions

2.1 LINEARITY AND PROBLEM SOLVING

The concept of linearity is an abstraction that is frequently used in the analysis of certain problems found in life. Many personal decisions involve the assumption of linear relationships even though we may not be conscious of these assumptions. From a practical standpoint, as long as decisions made on the basis of an informal, intuitive, and highly personalized analysis "work," there is little to be gained by questioning the assumptions. In business, however, problem solving often requires formal methods of analysis. Many individuals may be involved both in the analysis of the problem and in the application of the results. Where this is the case, it is important that assumptions concerning the relationships between factors in the problem be made explicit.

Inasmuch as linearity is one of the basic assumptions, a general knowledge of the concept is useful to the student of business. One should keep in mind, however, that the concept of linearity has many applications above and beyond those found in linear programming.

8

2.2 SYMBOLIC EXPRESSIONS FOR RELATIONSHIPS BETWEEN VARIABLES

Suppose that observation of certain phenomena convinces one that there is some relationship between factors X and Y. One method of expressing this relationship would be to describe it with words, that is, with a verbal model. For example, "it appears that the value of Y generally depends upon the value of X." Provided that a very general statement of this type is sufficient, words are an acceptable tool to use in describing the relationship between the variables. However, as the number of variables increases and their interrelationships become more complex, words become cumbersome and inadequate tools for model-building. Fortunately, this is a problem that mathematicians and statisticians solved long ago. The use of symbolic expressions is a second and more precise method for expressing relationships. Thus, the mathematician would simply write: $Y = F(X)$. These statements may be read as "the value of Y is a function of (depends on) the value of X," or more simply as "Y is a function of X." By convention, X is called the independent variable and Y the dependent variable, since the value of the latter depends on the value of the former.

Although the expression $Y = F(X)$ represents a notational improvement over the verbal description, it remains very general in the sense that we still do not know the exact nature of the relationship between the two variables. In one's attempt to solve business problems, for example, it is not too helpful to know only that "profits depend on sales."

2.3 MEANING OF LINEARITY

Linearity represents a special case of the relationship $Y = F(X)$. The relationship may be defined as linear if, for all pos-

sible values of X and Y, a given change in the value of X produces a *constant* change in the value of Y.

2.3.1 Nongraphical Interpretation

Consider the table of values given below:

TABLE 2.1

X	Change in X	Y	Change in Y
−3		−7	
−2	+1	−4	+3
−1	+1	−1	+3
0	+1	2	+3
1	+1	5	+3
2	+1	8	+3
3	+1	11	+3

In this example, $Y = F(X)$ is linear since a given change in
X (always +1) produces a constant change in the value of Y
(always +3).

Now consider this second table:

TABLE 2.2

X	Change in X	Y	Change in Y
0		0	
1	+1	1	+1
2	+1	4	+3
3	+1	9	+5
4	+1	16	+7

This relationship between X and Y is nonlinear, since the
change in X (always +1) produces varying changes in Y.

2.3.2 Graphical Interpretation

Plotting the data from Table 2.1 on a graph (Figure 2.1) reveals that all of the points lie on a straight line. The graph of a linear equation is always a straight line. The points of Table 2.2 form a curve rather than a straight line, thus indicating that this is a nonlinear relationship.

FIGURE 2.1

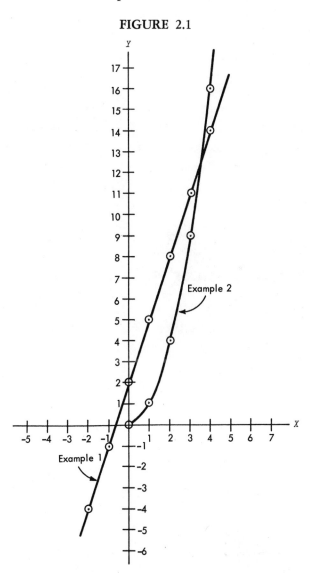

2.4 LINEAR EQUATIONS

The general expression of a linear function of one independent variable (slope intercept form) is $F(X) = a + b(X)$, usually written $Y = a + b(X)$ or $Y = a + bX$, where

> Y is the dependent variable,
> X is the independent variable,
> a is a numerical constant called the *intercept*, and
> b is a numerical constant called the *slope*.

The intercept a is the point where the line crosses the Y axis,
that is, it is the value for Y when X is zero. In Table 2.1 this oc-
curred at 2, that is, $a = 2$. The slope b of a linear function
(straight line) is the amount of change in Y caused by a *unit*
(1) change in X. In Table 2.1 each unit change in X produced
a change of $+3$ in the value for Y; thus, $b = 3$. The equation of
the function described in Table 2.1 is, therefore, $Y = 2 + 3(X)$
or $Y = 2 + 3X$.

2.5 DETERMINATION OF THE EQUATION OF A LINE

Occasionally it is necessary to find the equation of a line on
the basis of limited information. This can be done provided that
the coordinates are known for at least two points on the line. For
example, suppose that at point 1, $X = X_1$ and $Y = Y_1$ and that,
at point 2, $X = X_2$ and $Y = Y_2$ (where X_1, X_2, Y_1, and Y_2 are
specific values for X and Y). The change in Y from point 1 to
point 2 would be $(Y_2 - Y_1)$ and the change in X between the
two points would be $(X_2 - X_1)$. Dividing the total change in Y
by the total change in X between the points would give us the
change in Y per unit change in X, that is, the slope of the line,
namely,

$$b = \frac{Y_2 - Y_1}{X_2 - X_1}.$$

(2.1)

EXAMPLE. Suppose that the following points are known for a linear function:

At Point 1	*At Point 2*
$X_1 = 1, Y_1 = 5$	$X_2 = 3, Y_2 = 11$

Using Equation 2.1,

$$b = \frac{Y_2 - Y_1}{X_2 - X_1} = \frac{11 - 5}{3 - 1} = 3.$$

The general equation for a line is $Y = a + b(X)$. Since the specific value for b is now known, the expression for this particular function may now be written as $Y = a + 3(X)$ or $Y = a + 3X$.

To find the value of the intercept a, substitute the values for X and Y at one of the known points. For example, using point 1, where $X_1 = 1$ and $Y_1 = 5$,

$$Y = a + 3(X),$$
$$5 = a + 3(1),$$
$$a = 2.$$

The complete expression may now be written as

$$Y = 2 + 3(X).$$

2.6 DETERMINATION OF INTERCEPTS

In business one is frequently confronted with the problem of evaluating alternative courses of action, and interest frequently centers on the special case where the consequences of two or more alternatives are equal.

2.6.1 Graphical Determination of Intercepts

Consider the following linear equations, which have been plotted in Figure 2.2:

$$Y_1 = 2 + X_1 \tag{2.2}$$

$$Y_2 = 2X_2 \tag{2.3}$$

$$Y_3 = 10 - \frac{1}{2}X_3. \tag{2.4}$$

Note that Equation 2.4 has a negative slope, that is, the value of Y decreases as the value of X increases. This is the type of line most frequently encountered in the graphical method.

FIGURE 2.2

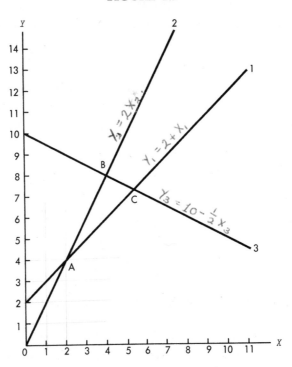

It is evident from the graph that the Y values for Equations (lines) 2.2 and 2.3 are equal $(Y_1 = Y_2 = 4)$ when X_1 and X_2 are both equal to 2. Similarly, Equations 2.3 and 2.4 "cross" at $X = 4$ and $Y = 8$. The intersection of Equations 2.2 and 2.4 is somewhat more difficult to determine precisely. Perhaps the best answer that could be given at this point is that their point of intersection is somewhere between the X values of 5 and 6 and the Y values of 7 and 9. Graphs typically do not produce precise results. If more accurate answers are required, one must resort to other methods of analysis.

2.6.2 Algebraic Solution for Intercepts

When two lines "cross" one another, this means that at that particular point (X value) the Y values are equal. At all other X values, of course, the corresponding Y values would be different. If we are interested only in the point of intersection (crossover), we can take advantage of this temporary equality.

At point A,

$$Y_1 = 2 + X,$$
$$Y_2 = 2X.$$

But we also know that $Y_1 = Y_2$ (at this special point only). Substitution gives us

$$Y_1 = Y_2,$$
$$2 + X = 2X,$$
$$2 = 2X - X,$$
$$2 = X$$

(value of X_1 and X_2 at intersection).

The value of Y that results from a value of $X = 2$ in both equations is

$$
\begin{aligned}
Y_1 &= 2 + X & Y_2 &= 2(X) \\
&= 2 + 2 & &= 2(2) \\
&= 4, & &= 4.
\end{aligned}
$$

At point B,

$$Y_2 = Y_3$$
$$2X = 10 - \frac{1}{2}X$$
$$2X + \frac{X}{2} = 10$$
$$\frac{5}{2}X = 10$$
$$X = 4.$$

$$Y_2 = 2X$$
$$= 2(4)$$
$$= 8$$
$$\text{Thus, } Y_3 = 10 - \frac{X}{2}$$
$$= 10 - \frac{4}{2}$$
$$= 8.$$

Develop your own solution for point C (the proper values are $X = 5\frac{1}{3}$ and $Y = 7\frac{1}{3}$).

2.7 EXERCISES

1. The following values are given for a function:

X	Y
2	26
4	22
7	16
12	6

a) Is this functional relationship linear? Why or why not?
b) What is the equation for this relationship?
c) Determine the X and Y intercepts.

2. The points identified below are known for a linear function:

At Point 1	*At Point 2*
$X = 5, Y = 30$	$X = 8, Y = 18$

a) What is the slope of this line?
b) Determine the equation for this function.
c) What are the X and Y intercepts?

3. Three linear functions are given as follows:

$$Y_1 = 32 - \frac{4}{5}X_1$$

$$Y_2 = \frac{3}{2}X_2$$

$$Y_3 = 8 + \frac{1}{2}X_3$$

a) Plot these equations on graph paper. Approximate the three intercepts from your plot.

b) Determine the intercepts directly from the equations, that is, develop an algebraic solution.

4. Mr. John Franklin is a salesman who drives his own car on company business. His employer reimburses him for such travel at the rate of 10¢ per mile. Franklin estimates that his fixed costs per year, such as taxes, insurance, and depreciation, are $517. The direct or variable costs, such as gas, oil, and lubrication, average about 4.5¢ per mile.

a) Draw a break-even chart (total annual cost vs. miles) and determine the number of miles Franklin must drive each year on company business to break even on total automobile expenses.

b) Determine his break-even point algebraically by finding the point of intersection for the equations that describe his "income" from driving the automobile and his total annual expense of owning and operating the automobile.

5. The Saveio Company is anticipating an order for a machined part. The size of the order has not yet been specified by the customer. Three manufacturing alternatives exist for producing this part. Method No. 1 will involve tooling costs of $180 and a direct cost per unit of $2.50. Method No. 2 involves more extensive tooling, having a cost of $390, but would reduce direct cost to $1.30 per unit. Method No. 3 involves no tooling

and utilizes direct labor only. The expected cost per unit using this alternative would be $3.90.

a) Determine the total cost per order and the cost per unit for each of the methods using the following order sizes: 60, 120, 200, 300.

b) Plot the total costs obtained from *a*) on graph. Determine from your graph the approximate order sizes at which the costs for the alternatives are equal.

c) Write a linear equation which describes the total cost per order for each manufacturing method. Use these equations to determine the exact order size at which total cost is equal.

d) What advantage does the use of equations in the analysis of this problem have over the tabular approach used in *a*) above? Explain.

3 | The Graphical Method

The graphical is the simplest and most easily understood of the several linear programming methods. For this reason it is a useful starting point in our discussion of programming fundamentals. As with most quantitative models, the price of simplicity is a reduction in applicability. Most management problems worth subjecting to formal analysis within a linear programming format would require one of the more complex and powerful solution methods to be described in Chapters 4 and 5.

A thorough knowledge of the graphical procedure should give the reader the insight and confidence necessary to understand what these more advanced methods accomplish and why they do so.

Like all linear programming methods, the graphical consists of a well-defined set of logical steps. By following this systematic procedure one can be certain of solving a problem with a minimum amount of computational effort. The basic steps or stages in the graphical solution method are as follows:

1. *Determine restrictions or constraints.*
2. *Select an appropriate objective function.*
3. *Solve for the optimal solution using either*

a) *direct graphical method, or*
b) *algebraic method for basic solutions.*
4. *Interpretation of optimal solution for implementation.*

Since this book focuses on making management decisions with the assistance of linear programming, it is important that you understand the meaning as well as the computational details of programming.

The nature and purpose of each of these steps in the solution procedure are best demonstrated by example. The remainder of this chapter will therefore demonstrate their application to a sample problem. At the end of each step you should check your comprehension of the material presented by working out the Self-Checking Problem suggested.

THE BAKER'S DECISION

The owner of a small bakery that specializes in cookies must decide what types and quantities of output to prepare for sale tomorrow. Let us assume there are only two kinds of cookies— sugar and iced cookies—from which he may select his product mix. We also assume that he will not have an opportunity to order additional supplies or hire additional helpers, so that to-morrow's product mix can only be produced with materials, la-bor, and equipment currently on hand.[1] These are as follows:

Cookie mix—120 pounds;
Icing mix— 32 pounds;
Baking equipment—oven with capacity of 120 dozen per day;
Bakery labor—15 hours.

---

[1] Limiting outputs to two products is necessary if the problem is to be solved using the graphical format. The limitation on ordering identifies this as an allocation problem, that is, the allocation of limited resources among alternative ends.

Finally, we need information about the process by which these resources are related to the alternative products.[2]

Required per Dozen	Iced	Sugar
Cookie mix	1.0 pounds	0.6 pounds
Icing mix	0.4 pounds	none
Labor	0.15 hours	0.10 hours

As noted earlier, the ovens are capable of handling 120 dozen cookies per day.[3]

3.1 DETERMINATION OF RESTRICTIONS (*STEP 1*)

Restrictions or constraints limit the number of possible alternatives available to the managerial decision maker. In the bakery example, each limited resource places certain limits on the kinds and quantities of products the baker can produce tomorrow. Determining the effects of these restrictions is the first step in the graphical solution method.

3.1.1 Determination of Cookie Mix Restriction

Each dozen iced cookies requires 1.0 pound and each dozen sugar cookies 0.6 pound of cookie mix. The total demand for this material tomorrow must be equal to or less than the 120-pound quantity available, as shown in Equation 3.1:

$$1.0 \, Q_I + .6 \, Q_S \leq 120, \tag{3.1}$$

[2] In most industries, this type of data would be drawn from bills of material, operations sheets, and other product and process design documents.

[3] Note that all data are given as single numbers rather than as probability distributions. Certainty is assumed.

where

Q_I = dozens of iced cookies,
Q_S = dozens of sugar cookies.

For example, should the baker elect to produce only sugar cookies, he has enough cookie mix on hand to produce a maximum of 200 dozen (120 ÷ 0.6). Similarly, it is not technically feasible to produce more than 120 dozen iced cookies (120 ÷ 1.0) if only iced cookies are produced. It is also possible, of course, to produce other mixes of these two products so long as total demand does not exceed 120 pounds. Several of these possible combinations are shown in Table 3.1.

TABLE 3.1

	Dozens		Cookie Mix (in pounds)		
Combination	Sugar	Iced	Sugar	Iced	Total
1	200	0	120	0	120
2	150	30	90	30	120
3	100	60	60	60	120
4	50	90	30	90	120
5	0	120	0	120	120

A key point illustrated in Table 3.1 is that, because of the restriction, the baker's decision will necessarily involve tradeoffs and compromises between the two products. For example, changing from combination one to two (adding 30 dozen iced cookies to the product mix) is possible only if sugar cookies are decreased by 50 dozen. Furthermore, this swapping takes place at a constant ratio of 30 to 50 for all of the combinations shown. This fact is not surprising since the ratio of this ingredient in the two products is 3 to 5 (0.6 to 1.0 in the recipes).[4] In the lan-

---

[4] If the rate of substitution were not constant, the constraint would

guage of linear programming the *exchange rate* or *physical rate of substitution* between the two variables (products) is three to five in terms of a particular mutually required resource (cookie mix in this instance). Substitution rates are a key concept in all programming methods and will be utilized in each subsequent chapter.

One advantage of the graphical method is that the effects of restrictions or constraints on a decision can be represented visually. Consider, for example, Figure 3.1 which represents a plot

FIGURE 3.1

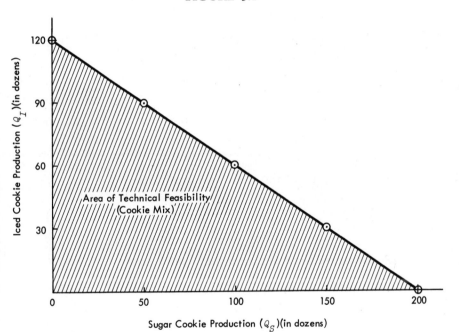

of the five combinations noted in Table 3.1. A number of important points can be made about restrictions based on this illustration:

---

not be a linear one. This would not fit one of the basic assumptions of linear programming.

1. All five points fall on the linear function defined by the two intercepts $(Q_s = 0, Q_I = 120)$ and $(200, 0)$. If a restriction is linear, only two points are needed to define the function.

2. The shaded area in Figure 3.1 includes all possible values for the two variables $(Q_s$ and $Q_I)$ which are feasible in terms of the cookie mix constraint. Thus, such combinations as $(50, 60)$, $(100, 50)$, and $(150, 25)$ are feasible because they plot between the origin and the restriction. Points that fall outside the shaded area $[(50, 120)\ (100, 90)\ (150, 60)]$ are not feasible since they would require more than the 120 pounds of cookie mix available.

3. The slope of the restriction is negative at the rate of three to five. This means that, in terms of the cookie mix restriction, 5 dozen sugar cookies may be substituted for 3 dozen iced cookies and vice versa. As noted earlier, this ratio was established by the data in the recipes (0.6 to 1.0). The display of Figure 3.1 does not add any new information about the problem, but simply allows us to visualize the implications of the mathematics for the management decision.

4. The equation of the restriction in slope intercept form is[5]

$$Q_I = 120 - \frac{0.6}{1.0} Q_s = 120 - \frac{3}{5} Q_s. \qquad (3.2)$$

3.1.2 Determination of Manpower Restriction

The 15 hours of bakery labor available might be allocated to the production of 100 dozen iced cookies $(15 \div 0.15)$, 150 dozen sugar cookies $(15 \div 0.10)$, or any combination that requires 15 or less labor hours. A graphical plot of this information is shown in Figure 3.2.[6] Note that this constraint is more severe than that

---

[5] The reader who has difficulty with this equation should review Sections 2.4 and 2.5.

[6] The equation of the direct labor constraint is

$$Q_I = 100 - \frac{0.10}{0.15} Q_s = 100 - \frac{2}{3} Q_s.$$

The rate of substitution is 2 to 3 for the labor resource.

FIGURE 3.2

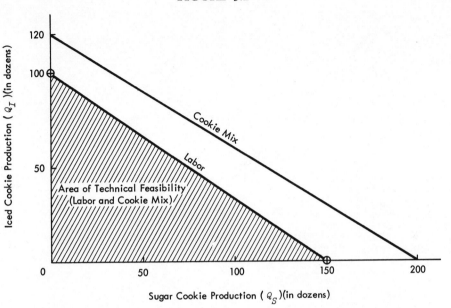

Sugar Cookie Production (Q_S)(in dozens)

for cookie mix. Expressed another way, the baker has more than enough cookie mix on hand to make any of the combinations permitted by the scarcer resource, direct labor. As a consequence, the area of technical feasibility in terms of these two limited resources becomes the area defined by the latter resource alone.[7] For this reason, we can omit cookie mix from the further stages of our analysis since it is not a binding or *relevant* restriction on this particular product mix decision.

3.1.3 Other Restrictions and the Feasibility Polygon

Figure 3.3 shows the effect of all relevant constraints on the baker's decision. The slope of the oven restriction is one to one and, for certain mixes, is more restrictive than labor. The two

---

[7] In the language of linear programming, the manpower constraint *dominates* the cookie mix restriction.

FIGURE 3.3

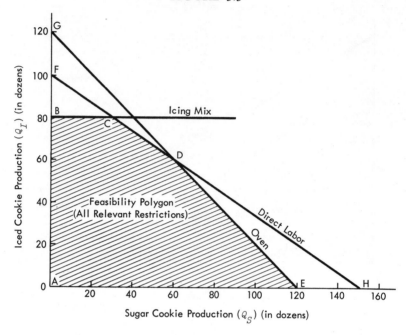

products (variables) can be substituted for one another in terms of this resource at a one to one ratio so long as the total requirement is 120 dozen per day or less. The equation of this restriction is $Q_I = 120 - Q_S$. Icing mix, on the other hand, is a constraint on the production of iced cookies only. There is no rate of substitution between the two variables relative to this limited resource, so that this equation is simply $Q_I = 80$.

One additional type of special restriction is needed in this and any other linear programming problem. We are interested only in *positive* values for decision variables (Q_S and Q_I in our example). In terms of pure mathematics, negative values for these variables (from other than the first quadrant) meet the technical requirement imposed by restrictions. For this reason we must add the seemingly obvious but important statement that $Q_S \geq 0$ and $Q_I \geq 0$.

3.1.4 Summary Comments of Restrictions

Some important points about the nature and role of restrictions are summarized below:

1. The general form in which all linear restrictions are expressed is

$$a_{11}x_1 + a_{12}x_2 \ldots \leq b_1, \tag{3.3}$$
$$a_{21}x_1 + a_{22}x_2 \ldots \leq b_2.$$

An equation of this form is needed for each limited resource in the problem. In our bakery example the three relevant inequalities are

$$0.15\, Q_I + 0.10\, Q_S \leq 15, \tag{3.4}$$
$$1.0\ \ Q_I + 1.0\ \ Q_S \leq 120, \tag{3.5}$$
$$0.4\ \ Q_I + 0.0\ \ Q_S \leq 32. \tag{3.6}$$

In addition, as noted earlier, we wish to limit our analysis to positive values for the decision variables, so that

$$Q_I \geq 0, Q_S \geq 0. \tag{3.7}$$

Where there are only two independent variables, as in our example, these linear restrictions can be shown graphically as in Figure 3.3.

2. The analysis may be limited to those restrictions which are *relevant* to the problem. In our example we found that cookie mix is not relevant, that is, it does not define one of the boundaries for the feasibility polygon. While there is no real harm in carrying nonrelevant factors through an analysis, they only add to the computational workload—an unwelcome task when hand computations are involved.

3. The relevant restrictions which are *critical* at a particular stage in the analysis will vary. For example, if a baker is considering product mixes which emphasize iced cookies, the icing mix

constraint is most likely to be critical (Figure 3.3). If sugar cookies are emphasized, the oven is more likely to be the critical restriction on his decision.

4. The general effect of all restrictions is to limit the number of alternatives. Only those alternatives which plot within the feasibility polygon (satisfy the constraints) are acceptable solutions (decisions). An examination of Figure 3.3, however, indicates that the baker still has many possible product mixes open to him. What is needed now is a means of measuring the relative desirability of these alternatives. This is the purpose of the objective function in linear programming and takes us to *Step 2* in the graphical procedure.

CHECKING YOUR COMPREHENSION

(Answers will be found at the end of the book)

Check your understanding of the material presented in Section 3.1 by using the problem outlined below. Answers will be found on p. 138.

THE ZEUS COMPANY (A)

The Zeus Company manufactures a deluxe and a standard model to stock in advance of customer orders. Current market conditions make it possible to sell any combination of products which can be produced. An optimal product mix is desired.

The manufacturing process for these products is relatively simple. Both models require a machining operation, and the deluxe model requires an additional painting operation. The same machine tools are used for fabricating both models. Since all units are placed in inventory before being sold, warehouse space as well as equipment capacities must be considered in making the product mix decisions.

Process requirements and capacities for the next month are as follows:

Resource Requirements	Standard Unit	Deluxe Unit	Capacity Available
Machine hours	2	3	24,000
Square feet of warehousing	4	3	36,000
Man hours for painting	0	1	6,000

Questions 1 to 4: The Zeus Company (A)

1. State in words the relationship between the machining requirements for the two products and total machine capacity available next month.

2. Using Equation 3.1 (p. 22) as a guide, write the inequality which describes this relationship.

3. Plot your results on graph paper (deluxe units on the vertical axis). Identify the area of technical feasibility for next month's product mix in terms of the machine resource.

4. Using Equation 3.2 (p. 24) as a guide, write the equation of the machine capacity restriction in slope intercept form. Identify both intercepts and the exchange rate between the two variables.

SUGGESTION TO THE READER. Check your answers to Questions 1 to 4 on p. 138 before trying to answer 5 to 8.

Questions 5 to 8: The Zeus Company (A)

5. Write the inequalities which describe the relationship between the two variables and the warehousing and painting capacities for next month.

6. Write the equations of these restrictions in slope intercept

form. Identify the intercepts and rates of substitution between the two products for each constraint.

7. Plot the three restrictions which limit the product mix decision for the Zeus Company (deluxe units on vertical axis). Shade in the feasibility polygon. List several combinations which are feasible and several which are not feasible.

8. Which of the limited resources will most likely be the "bottleneck" next month if standard units are emphasized in the product mix? Deluxe model?

3.2 SELECTION OF OBJECTIVE FUNCTION (*STEP* 2)

Problem solving using linear programming methods is not different from problem solving in general. Once a set of alternative courses of action has been defined, comparison and evaluation takes place by measuring the consequences of each alternative against an objective or desired result. In linear programming the desired result must be expressed in the form of a linear equation which is most often referred to as the *objective function* or *measure of effectiveness*.

One way in which the baker might express his highest-order economic objective would be the maximization of return on investment. Figure 3.4 outlines the factors and computations involved in this approach. In equation form we can express return on investment (ROI) as

$$ROI = \text{Investment Turnover times Profit Margin, or}$$

$$IT \times PM = \frac{SR}{I} \times \frac{P}{SR} = \frac{(SR - TC)}{I}$$

$$= \frac{SR - (VC + FC)}{I}$$

$$= \frac{(SR - VC) - FC}{I}. \tag{3.8}$$

If we assume that the baker's fixed costs and investment are

FIGURE 3.4

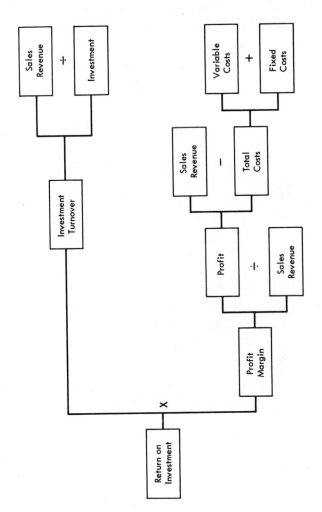

relatively fixed, we can maximize *ROI* over short time periods by maximizing $(SR - VC)$, the contribution margin for all products produced and sold.

Suppose the selling price for iced cookies is 70¢ and the direct or variable material and labor cost is 50¢ per dozen. We also assume the corresponding data for sugar cookies to be 60¢ and 45¢ respectively. Every dozen iced cookies produced and sold will contribute 20¢ to fixed costs (at all quantities below the break-even point) or to profit (for outputs above the break-even volume).[8] In like manner, the margin or "contribution" of sugar cookies is 15¢ per dozen. Thus, an appropriate economic objective for the baker's decision on tomorrow's product mix should be

$$TC = C_I \times Q_I + C_S \times Q_S, \tag{3.9}$$

where

TC = total dollar contribution
C_I = contribution of iced cookies (per dozen)
Q_I = production of iced cookies (dozens)
C_S = contribution of sugar cookies (per dozen)
Q_S = production of sugar cookies (dozens)

Since the contributions of both products are known, the specific objective function for the programming problem may be written as:

$$(\text{max.}) \ TC = 0.20 \ Q_I + 0.15 \ Q_S \tag{3.10}$$

Our task now is to develop a search procedure for those *unique* values for Q_I and Q_S which (1) fall within the polygon of

---

[8] The measure of economic effectiveness in a linear programming problem must be expressed in the form of a linear function. For this reason the model normally incorporates variable costs only. Fixed costs must usually be handled by analysis above and beyond the programming formulation.

technical feasibility, that is, satisfy the restrictions stated in Equations 3.4, 3.5, and 3.6, and also (2) *maximize* total dollar contributions as expressed in Equation 3.10. Several methods for performing this task will be discussed in the following section which describes *Step 3* in the graphical procedure.

CHECKING YOUR COMPREHENSION

(Answers will be found at the end of the book)

Gauge your understanding of Section 3.2 by answering the following questions. Check your answers on p. 140.

THE ZEUS COMPANY (B)

The expected price for the deluxe model during the next month will be $12 per unit. The standard model will be priced at $8 per unit.

Direct labor and material charges for production of each deluxe unit are expected to be about $9, while the standard unit will cost approximately $7 per unit to manufacture.

No major additions to plant or warehouse capacity are planned for the coming month. Past experience with fixed costs of the plant indicate that they are relatively independent of product mix.

Questions 9 and 10: The Zeus Company (B)

9. Write the linear equation which best describes the objective function for the Zeus product mix decision.
10. What conditions must product mix meet with respect to the restrictions and objective function?

3.3 OPTIMAL SOLUTION METHODS (*STEP 3*)

An optimal solution to a linear programming problem represents those values for the decision variables which (1) satisfy the relevant linear restrictions for the problem, and (2) maximize or minimize an appropriate linear objective function. In our graphical example, this means finding those unique values for Q_S and Q_I which fall within the feasibility polygon and also maximize total dollar contribution. As Figure 3.3 indicates, there is a very large number of product mix decisions which meet the feasibility criterion noted above.

One method of determining the optimal solution would be by trial and error. By inserting different feasible combinations in Equation 3.10, we might eventually discover those values which represent the best possible solution. An alternative would be to use one of the solution methods to be described in the following pages. These methods, like any of the several basic programming methods, make it possible to determine the optimal solution with the least possible computational effort. Linear programming may, in fact, be described as an effective and efficient search procedure for determining optimal solutions to types of problems in which there are more unknowns than linear equations.

As an interesting sidelight before proceeding with these solution methods, suppose we attempt an intuitive decision. One might reason, for example, that since the contribution of one product is higher than that of the other, a "good" solution would be to (1) produce as many iced cookies as possible, and (2) use any remaining resources to produce sugar cookies. This logic would lead us to produce 80 dozen iced cookies and 30 dozen sugar cookies as indicated by point C in Figure 3.3. The total contribution associated with this product mix would be $20.50. While such a decision is feasible and appears to make intuitive sense, does it yield a maximum contribution? The solution methods that follow will provide us with a basis for answering this question. More important, an understanding of graphical solution methods will give the reader considerable insight into the more powerful programming methods to be described in Chapters 4 and 5.

3.3.1 Direct Graphical Solution

Suppose we pick some arbitrary value for the objective function, say, $6.00, and compute several output combinations which would yield this amount (Table 3.2). If the values of Table 3.2 are plotted on a graph (Figure 3.5), they trace a straight line of the equation $Q_I = 30 - \frac{3}{4}(Q_S)$. This is not surprising, since Equation 3.10 is a linear function. Furthermore, the slope of the line is the contribution ratio for the products $(0.15 \div 20 = \frac{3}{4})$. Points on this line, then, represent solutions that are feasible

TABLE 3.2

Mix	Production (in dozens)		Contribution		
	Iced	Sugar	Iced	Sugar	Total
1......	30	0	$6.00	$0.00	$6.00
2......	24	8	4.80	1.20	6.00
3......	18	16	3.60	2.40	6.00
4......	6	32	1.20	4.80	6.00
5......	0	40	0.00	6.00	6.00

FIGURE 3.5

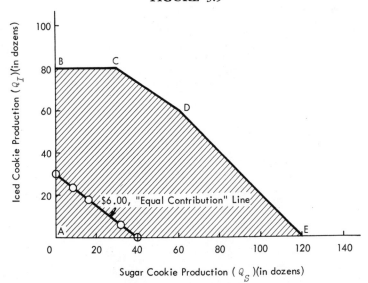

Sugar Cookie Production (Q_S)(in dozens)

and result in a total contribution of $6.00. Our aim, however, is to maximize the objective function; therefore these do not appear to be optimal solutions.

In Figure 3.6, the lines of "equal contribution" have been drawn in for $12.00, $18.00 and $21.00. These lines are parallel since their slopes are equal. It is necessary to dash a portion of the $18.00 line since some of those combinations represent solutions that are not technically feasible. Were we to continue drawing parallel lines farther out from the origin, the solutions outside the area of technical feasibility would increase. Finally, a line would just intersect one point on the polygon (see $21.00 line at point D). The optimal solution indicated on the axes is 60 dozen each of sugar and iced cookies; the corresponding profit is $21.00.

We can generalize from this illustration and make a key point which is essential for understanding all linear programming methods. The optimal solution will always occur at one of the

FIGURE 3.6

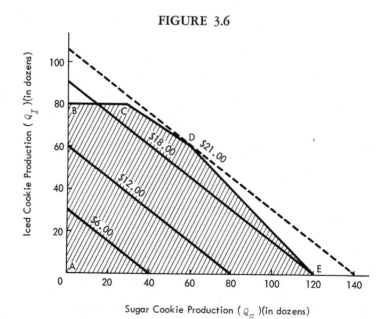

Sugar Cookie Production (Q_S)(in dozens)

vertices on the feasibility polygon.[9] The term *basic solutions* is often applied to the values for the variables at these points. Knowing that the optimal solution will always be found here is extremely useful since we can now limit our search to these points and still be certain of finding the optimal solution. This is one of the ways in which linear programming "pays off" on its promise of minimum computational effort.

3.3.2 Algebraic Solution

Given the insight gained in the above section, a second and more direct method for solving the simple problems which lend themselves to graphical formats would be to compute the limited number of basic solutions, and to test each set of values in the objective function.

The coordinates of points B, C, D, and E in Figure 3.6 may be approximated directly from the graph. If more precision is needed, they should be computed using the equations for the various relevant constraints and the method of Section 2.6 for determining the intersection of two linear functions. These co-ordinates and the corresponding value of the objective function are shown in Table 3.3. As expected, the optimal solution is point D which calls for the production tomorrow of 60 dozen each of iced and sugar cookies.

TABLE 3.3

| Point | Dozens of Cookies | | Contribution |
	Iced	Sugar	
A	0	0	$ 0.00
B	80	0	16.00
C	80	30	20.50
D	60	60	21.00
E	0	120	18.00

[9] In the special case when the slope of the "equal contribution" lines is the same as that of one of the constraints, there will be a range of optimal solutions.

3.3.3   Summary Comments on Solution Methods

The graphical solution method outlined above seems and is cumbersome. However, it is important that the beginner go through this routine at least once so that he understands why optimal solutions always lie on the perimeter of the feasibility polygon. Once this point has been established, one can utilize the more efficient algebraic solution method which tests the limited number of basic solutions against the objective function directly.

The fact that both methods indicate point D rather than point C to be the optimal solution (as suggested by the intuitive analysis described earlier) also illustrates an important point. Intuitive solutions, even for relatively simple problems such as our bakery example, are often "good" but seldom optimal. Formal analysis of allocation problems using linear programming is most appropriate when the number of decision variables and restrictions is so large that intuitive methods cannot cope with the complexities of the decision. For this reason most real management problems require the more comprehensive programming methods to be described in Chapters 4 and 5.

CHECKING YOUR COMPREHENSION

(Answers will be found at the end of the book)

Use the questions below about the Zeus Company problem to evaluate your understanding of Section 3.3. Answers are on p. 140.

Questions *11* to *14:* The Zeus Company

11. Using Figure 3.6 as a guide, plot the Zeus objective function on your feasibility polygon for values of $6,000, $9,000, and $12,000. Plot additional lines as needed until you have identified the optimal solution.

12. Explain in your own words why optimal solutions are (a) *always* found on the rim of the polygon, and (b) except in special cases, found at the points (basic solutions) of the polygon. Describe the *special case* where a range of optimal solutions could exist.

13. Use your equations for the three restrictions to compute the values of Q_S and Q_D at the vertices of the polygon.

14. Using Table 3.3 as a guide, compute the value of the objective function at each of the basic solutions (vertices) of the polygon. Check the optimal solution indicated by this method against your answer to question 11 above.

3.4 INTERPRETATION OF SOLUTION (*STEP* 4)

In Section 3.3 it was shown that the optimal solution to the baker's product mix decision is that represented by point D in Figure 3.3. This solution calls for the production of 60 dozen each of iced and sugar cookies with a corresponding value for the objective function of $21.00. Is this all of the information we can give the decision maker from our linear programming analysis? Presumably he might wish to exercise his judgment on certain human or nonquantitative factors which are relevant to the decision but could not be included in the linear programming model of the problem.

The decision-maker might, for example, be most interested in knowing which restrictions will represent his "bottlenecks" and which resources will not be fully utilized. In linear programming extra or unused resources are referred to as *slack*. Table 3.4 shows that both labor and ovens will be fully utilized if the optimal mix is produced while extra slack cookie and icing mix will remain on hand at the end of the day. This suggests that the bakery's inventory policy may be inconsistent with the product mix.

The decision-maker may also be interested in knowing what

TABLE 3.4

	Cookie Mix (pounds)	Icing Mix (pounds)	Labor (hours)	Oven (dozen per day)
Sugar	36	0	6.0	60
Iced	60	24	9.0	60
Total	96	24	15.0	120
Capacity	120	32	15.0	120
"Slack"	24	8	0	0

the consequences would be of producing some mix of products other than the optimal one indicated by the linear programming model. For example, there may be special considerations of sales commitments, labor relations, and so forth which he feels must be considered in making a final decision. Linear programming cannot make such decisions based on qualitative factors, but it can assist in placing these factors in economic perspective. Suppose, for example, that the baker feels there are important reasons for increasing the percentage of iced cookies in the mix for tomorrow. Table 3.5 lists for each basic solution the loss in contribution or opportunity cost associated with choosing that alternative rather than the model's optimal solution of point D. If the decision-maker feels that the tangible and/or intangible benefits of producing 80 dozen iced cookies are worth more than 50¢ per day, he would be making a rational and logical decision to choose that alternative. Thus, one of the useful interpre-

TABLE 3.5

Point	Production (dozen) Iced	Production (dozen) Sugar	Dollar Contribution	Opportunity Cost
A	0	0	$ 0.00	$21.00
B	80	0	16.00	5.00
C	80	30	20.50	0.50
D	60	60	21.00	0.00
E	0	120	18.00	3.00

tations which the linear programmer can give to the decision-maker is some indication of the sensitivity of the model's objective function to variations from the optimal solution.

3.5 SUMMARY

The graphical method is capable of handling linear programming problems of only limited complexity and is, therefore, a special rather than a general method. The chief limiting factor is the number of variables involved. A two-dimensional graphical display of relationships is restricted to two independent variables.

The two basic assumptions common to all linear programming methods—linearity and certainty—are recognized explicitly both in framing the problem and in solving it.

Except in special cases, the optimal solution will always lie at one of the several points or vertices of the polygon of technical feasibility. The search for these points is made more effective by the visual display of the relationships among variables and constraints.

The precision of solutions developed by purely graphical solution methods is a function of the scale and accuracy of the graphical display. The accuracy of solutions may be improved through the use of algebraic methods. In such cases the graphical portion of the analysis becomes of secondary importance.

Most of the technical and economic phases of a problem may be expressed explicitly and treated directly in the analysis. Many qualitative and intangible human factors cannot be handled in this manner. The primary contribution of any quantitative method is that of narrowing the judgment portion of decision-making, not of eliminating it. It is important, therefore, to recognize that the optimal solution from a linear programming model is not necessarily an optimal overall solution to the problem. Managerial judgment rather than mathematics must be used in large part for the selection of the best alternative course of action and, of course, for the implementation of the decision.

3.6 REVIEW QUESTIONS

1. What is the general effect of any restriction or constraint on the number of alternatives open to a decision-maker?
2. Are all constraints on a decision relevant in a linear programming analysis?
3. What is a basic solution?
4. Why, except in special cases, is the optimal solution always at one of the points or vertices of the feasibility polygon?
5. Under what special circumstances could there be a range of optimal solutions to a graphical problem? Of what value would this information be to a decision-maker?
6. Linear programming is sometimes described as an effective search procedure. Explain the meaning of this statement.
7. Explain briefly where the two basic assumptions of linearity and certainty are reflected in a graphical analysis.

3.7 EXERCISES

1. Given the set of relevant constraints developed in this chapter for the bakery decision, what changes, if any, in the optimal product mix would result if the contributions of the two products were changed as follows:

a) $C_I = 25¢$ and $C_8 = 15¢$ (*Answers:* Point C)
b) $C_I = 30¢$ and $C_8 = 20¢$ (*Answers:* Points C to D)
c) $C_I = 21¢$ and $C_8 = 15¢$ (*Answers:* Point D)
d) $C_I = 20¢$ and $C_8 = 21¢$ (*Answers:* Point E)

2. Suppose that, for some reason, the capacity of the baker's oven is temporarily reduced from 120 dozen to only 100 dozen

per day. Assuming that all other constraints and contributions remain unchanged, what changes, if any, would this have on the optimal product mix? (*Answer:* $Q_I = 80$, $Q_s = 20$)

3. The Lotanoiz Corporation manufactures a "Hollywood" automobile muffler in one size only. However, it produces two models—the "Long-Life" and the "Economuf." The "Long-Life" is of heavier metal construction and also receives a special alloy dipping before being painted.

Since the corporation is young and operates on a comparatively small margin of profit, the owner–managers are very anxious to find the exact product mix that will yield a maximum return. At present, both types of mufflers are selling quite well and neither model seems to have the better market potential.

Comparison of Fabrication Time and Cost

| | | Time Required (hours per pair) | | |
Model	Total Direct Man Hours per Unit	Dipping Operation	Painting	Contribution per Unit
Economuf	1.0	—	0.1	$0.80
Long-Life	1.5	0.2	0.1	0.90

Painting operations may be carried on 37.5 hours per week. Two units are painted at a time. The dipping operation can be carried on 8 hours per day (5 days per week). Two units may be dipped at a time. As both mufflers have the same size, the shipping department can process up to 800 units weekly regardless of the model mix. A total of 900 man-hours is available per week in the fabricating department.

a) Given the information provided above, what weekly production schedule would you suggest?

b) Which departments will be operating at capacity if your schedule is adopted? How much idle capacity will exist in those departments that are operating at less than full capacity?

c) What could the management of the Lotanoiz Corporation do to "relax" the various technical restrictions in this problem, that is, to move the restrictions farther away from the origin? To which ones should their initial efforts be directed? Why?

4. The Plummer Company produces two types of men's billfolds. The higher-priced Chieftain line uses more first-grade materials and is virtually handmade. The lower-priced Warrior line is largely machinemade and uses a higher percentage of standard grade materials. Each Chieftain unit contributes $5.00 and each Warrior unit contributes $3.00 toward overhead and profit.

The firm has been producing 600 of the Chieftain model and 300 of the Warrior model every week. The most recent sales forecast indicates that these figures represent maximum possible sales during the next week as well. The company's labor force of ten skilled long-service employees works 36-hour weeks.

The company's suppliers have just notified it that, due to a temporary shortage of materials, no shipments can be made for at least one week. This means that the materials now available, the sales forecast, and labor availability must be considered in developing next week's schedule.

The material requirements and labor hour availability are as follows:

Resource Requirements	Required per Unit		Total Available This Week
	Chieftain	Warrior	
1st-grade materials (sq. ft)	0.4	0.2	256
Standard materials (sq. ft.)	0.3	0.5	276
Labor (hours)	0.5	0.2	360

a) The sales manager has proposed that only Chieftain models be produced next week because of its higher contribution. (1) Frame the problem in a graphical format. (2) Evaluate the sales manager's proposal.

b) The production engineer suggests that any reduction of work hours should be held to an absolute minimum. He proposes that the schedule adopted should be that which will maximize the number of employees' hours to be worked during the week. Evaluate this proposal.

4 The Simplex Method

4.1 GENERAL NATURE OF THE METHOD

The simplex is the general method of linear programming as differentiated from the graphical, transportation, and other special methods. Any problem that fits the two basic assumptions of linearity and certainty can be solved by this method. This broad problem solving capability is gained, from the student's viewpoint at least, only at the expense of a considerable increase in mathematical complexity. The term "simplex" is derived from the fact that this method is based on the so-called simplex algorithm. While it is more difficult to comprehend, the reader who fully understands the graphical method should be able to comprehend and perform the computational routine involved.

The basic problem in linear programming is to find the particular set of variables that satisfies all constraints and maximizes—or minimizes—the value of the objective function. The orderly solution of problems using the simplex format requires the performance of a series of carefully defined steps. The purpose of the procedure is to produce the desired result with minimum computational effort.

The major advantage of the graphical method is that the visual display of relationships enables the analyst to see the points (vertices) on the polygon of technical feasibility. Since the optimal solution ordinarily lies at one of these vertices, the search procedure may be limited to an analysis of these. Theoretically, a three-dimensional display might be useful for problems involving three variables. Constraints in this case would become planes, as would objective function, and the optimal solution would represent one of the many intersections generated by these planes.

Most linear programming problems that lend themselves to analysis by the simplex method involve many more than three variables. It would be most difficult to visualize a five-dimensional, let alone a twenty-dimensional problem. Nevertheless, it is useful in understanding the rationale of the simplex method to attempt certain analogies. One such analogy is to compare the computation procedure to that of developing a plan for climbing a mountain. The objective may be stated simply: to reach the summit (maximize the objective function). There would presumably be an infinite number of routes that might be taken by the climbers. If the mountain were high, it might be necessary to accomplish the total task in stages. Intuitive reasoning would indicate that, as long as each camp is higher up on the mountain than the previous one, the party will progress toward the summit. Starting from the base (origin), an effective climbing procedure (computation procedure) would enable the climbers to reach the summit (optimal solution) with a minimum number of camps (steps or iterations).

The computational procedure for the simplex method consists of a set of well-defined and logical steps. The general nature and sequence of these steps are as follows:

1. *Frame the problem.*

    a) Select relevant variables and restrictions. Express relationships between all variables and restrictions in equation form.

b) Determine an objective function or measure of effectiveness.

2. *Develop an initial feasible solution.*

   a) A feasible solution is one which does not violate any of the restrictions or constraints.

   b) For practical purposes the origin solution is usually selected.

3. *Evaluate alternative variables that might be brought into the solution.* If favorable alternatives are found, select the most favorable for implementation.

4. *Develop revised equations which express the new relationships between variables and restrictions.*

5. *Repeat steps 3 and 4 until analysis in step 3 indicates no additional favorable alternatives.*

6. *Interpret optimal solution for implementation.*

The specific nature and method of these steps will again be illustrated by example. Since the simplex method relies completely on mathematics, its logic and meaning are not always intuitively obvious. For this reason we will use the baker's decision as our sample problem and, wherever possible, point out analogies between the simplex and graphical methods.[1]

4.2 FRAMING THE PROBLEM (*STEP 1*)

The data which describe a complex allocation problem must first be organized in a logical fashion so that the procedures involved in the computational routine can be applied in a systematic way.

---

[1] Remember that the graphical is actually a special case of the more general simplex method which can be applied when only two variables are involved.

4.2.1 Determination of Relevant Variables, and Restrictions

The three relevant inequalities in the baker's decision were identified in Chapter 3 as Equations 3.4, 3.5, and 3.6.[2] These inequalities were

$$\text{Labor:} \quad 0.15\,Q_I + 0.10\,Q_S \le 15 \tag{4.1}$$
$$\text{Ovens:} \quad 1.0 \quad Q_I + 1.0 \quad Q_S \le 120 \tag{4.2}$$
$$\text{Icing mix:} \quad 0.4 \quad Q_I + 0.0 \quad Q_S \le 32. \tag{4.3}$$

The simplex routine requires the use of equations rather than inequalities. This conversion can be accomplished by utilizing another concept introduced in Chapter 3—that of slack or unused resources. For example,

$$0.15\,Q_I + 0.10\,Q_S + \text{slack labor hours} = 15. \tag{4.4}$$

Equation 4.4 states that the labor hours needed for the production of iced and sugar cookies plus those not needed for these products (unused or slack) will be equal to the 15 total labor hours available. The amount of slack labor thus depends on the amount of labor "left over" in the product mix.

For computation purposes it is necessary to express the slack capacity in the same general form as the real variables. A useful convention is to assume that fictitious products are made with those capacities not required by the real variables in the solution. For example, suppose that some imaginary cookie (type L) can be produced with the slack labor capacity. The symbol Q_L would represent the number of dozens produced. If each dozen L cookies is assumed to require 1.0 hour of labor capacity and no other resources, then $1.0\,Q_L$ represents the demand on the

---

[2] In Chapter 3, the cookie mix constraint was shown not to be relevant. In order to keep our illustrations here as simple as possible, we will assume that this information is available prior to use of the simplex techniques.

labor resource to produce Q_L dozens.[3] The supply and demand equation for the labor resource may now be written as

$$0.15\,Q_I + 0.10\,Q_S + 1.0\,Q_L = 15. \tag{4.5}$$

This equation means that the sum of the labor requirements for iced, sugar, and L cookies is always equal to 15 hours. The requirement for L cookies is a mathematical fact, but a fiction in reality, since it actually represents that portion of labor capacity not required for the real variables.

Let O cookies represent the slack variable for unused oven capacity and M cookies the corresponding slack variable for icing mix.[4] The complete set of relationships between all five variables —two real and three slack—and the labor constraint may now be expressed as follows:

$$0.15\,Q_I + 0.10\,Q_S + 1.0\,Q_L + 0\,Q_O + 0\,Q_M = 15, \tag{4.6}$$

where

$$
\left.
\begin{aligned}
Q_I &= \text{dozens of iced cookies} \\
Q_S &= \text{dozens of sugar cookies}
\end{aligned}
\right\} \text{real variables}
$$

$$
\left.
\begin{aligned}
Q_L &= \text{dozens of } L \text{ cookies} \\
Q_O &= \text{dozens of } O \text{ cookies} \\
Q_M &= \text{dozens of } M \text{ cookies}
\end{aligned}
\right\} \text{slack variables}
$$

Equation 4.6 differs from Equation 4.5 only in that the relationship between the two slack variables representing oven and icing mix resources have been added to the expression. Their

---

[3] The assumption of 1.0 labor hour is based on computation convenience. Technically, any positive number would be an acceptable assumption. Note that slack variables are assumed to require only the resource for which they represent idle capacity. Thus, the "recipe" for L cookies calls for 1.0 hour of labor capacity and zero icing mix and oven capacity.

[4] Using the procedure suggested in Footnote 3, the "recipe" for O cookies calls for 1.0 unit of oven capacity per dozen. Making M cookies requires 1.0 pounds of icing mix per dozen.

coefficients are zero since their production requires no labor capacity. The addition of these two terms does not add to the "practical" meaning of the equation, but it does satisfy one of the basic requirements of the simplex method—that all relationships between variables and restrictions must be stated explicitly and completely.

Similar expressions representing the relationship between all five variables and the oven and icing mix capacities may now be derived. For example, O cookies, the slack variable representing oven capacity not required for real products, is assumed for computational convenience to require 1.0 unit of oven capacity per dozen and no other resources. Thus,

$$1.0\, Q_I + 1.0\, Q_S + 1.0\, Q_O = 120. \tag{4.7}$$

Finally, we must complete the statement by including terms for the two additional slack variables (L and M cookies) so that all possible relationships are specified:

$$1.0\, Q_I + 1.0\, Q_S + 0\, Q_L + 1.0\, Q_O + 0\, Q_M = 120. \tag{4.8}$$

The coefficients for Q_L and Q_M are zero since, by definition, these slack variables require no oven capacity, that is, only labor is required for L cookies and only icing mix for M cookies.

The amount of icing mix on hand is 32 pounds. Only one real, iced cookies, and one slack variable, M cookies (the slack variable for icing mix), make demands on this resource. The recipe for iced cookies specifies 0.4 pound per dozen. By definition, we assume that 1.0 pounds of mix are needed to "produce" one dozen M cookies. The complete equation would be

$$0.4\, Q_I + 0\, Q_S + 0\, Q_L + 0\, Q_O + 1.0\, Q_M = 32. \tag{4.9}$$

We now have three equations (4.6, 4.8, and 4.9) which describe explicitly and completely the set of relationships between all variables (two real and three slack) and all relevant restrictions.[5] Any set of values for the five variables which satisfies these three equations is a *feasible solution* to the problem.[6]

It is more convenient for computation purposes to express the relationships between variables and constraints in the form of a table than to retain the expressions in their more familiar equation form. The general format for such a presentation is given in Table 4.1.

TABLE 4.1

Variables	Q_I	Q_S	Q_L	Q_O	Q_M	Capacity
Labor	0.15	0.10	1	0	0	15
Oven	1.0	1.0	0	1	0	120
Icing Mix	0.4	0.0	0	0	1	32

The columns in the table represent the recipes for the various products (variables) in the problem. For example, reading down the column headed by the symbol Q_I reproduces the requirements for iced cookies, 0.15 labor hours, 1.0 unit of oven capacity, and 0.4 pounds of icing mix per dozen. Similarly, each dozen sugar cookies requires 0.10 labor hours, 1.0 unit of oven capacity, and zero icing mix. The requirements for all slack variables are unique in that, by definition, they require 1.0 unit of the capacity they represent and nothing more. Just as sugar cookies require no icing mix, L (the variable that represents slack labor capacity) cookies require no oven capacity or icing mix. In like manner, O cookies require only oven capacity and M cookies require icing mix but no labor or oven capacity.

Equations 4.6, 4.8, and 4.9 may be reproduced from Table 4.1 by multiplying each of the series of coefficients in each row by

---

[5] Technically, we should also note that all variables (including slacks) must be equal to or greater than zero.

[6] The "feasibility polygon" for the simplex method is defined by a set of equations.

the appropriate Q, which appears at the head of each column. For example, the first row produces

$$(0.15)\ Q_I + (0.10)\ Q_S + (1)\ Q_L + (0)\ Q_O + (0)\ Q_M = 15.$$

Similar interpretation shows that the second row reproduces Equation 4.8, and that the third row represents Equation 4.9.

4.2.2   Selection of Objective Function

The general form of the objective function for the baker's product mix decision was formulated in Chapter 3 as

$$(\text{max.})\ TC = Q_I \times C_I + Q_S \times C_S,$$

where

$TC =$ total dollar contribution,
$C_I =$ contribution per dozen iced cookies, and
$C_S =$ contribution per dozen sugar cookies.

The simplex analysis, however, has introduced three new (slack) variables into the problem. Thus, a complete statement of the objective function must include the "contribution" of the slack as well as the real variables:

$$Q_I \times C_I + Q_S \times C_S + Q_L \times C_L + Q_O \times C_O + Q_M \times C_M = TC.$$

What values should be assigned to C_L, C_O, and C_M, that is, what addition to the total dollar contribution results from the addition of one dozen L, O, or M cookies to the product mix? Since these are fictitious products introduced to represent slack capacity, their economic contribution should represent the value of slack capacity. By implication, the contribution of slack resources in the graphical method was zero; unused capacity resulted in no additional income or costs. In accordance with the need for explicit relationships in the simplex method, assume that C_L, C_o, and C_M are zero. Thus,

$$Q_I \times 20\cent + Q_s \times 15\cent + Q_L \times 0\cent + Q_o \times 0\cent +$$
$$Q_M \times 0\cent = TC. \tag{4.10}$$

This information concerning the relative economic values of the variables can now be added to the computation table. By convention these values are placed above the corresponding Q term at the head of each column, as in Table 4.2.

TABLE 4.2

Contribution Variables	20¢ Q_I	15¢ Q_s	0¢ Q_L	0¢ Q_o	0¢ Q_M	Capacity
Labor	0.15	0.10	1	0	0	15
Oven	1.0	1.0	0	1	0	120
Icing Mix	0.4	0.0	0	0	1	32

The information presented in Table 4.2 can be summarized as follows:

a) There are five variables in the problem. Only two of these (iced and sugar cookies) are real variables. The three slack variables (*L*, *O*, and *M* cookies) are fictitious products introduced into the problem because of the necessity for explicit relationships. In reality, these slack variables represent unused or idle capacity in the labor, oven, and icing mix resources.

b) The numbers in the columns below each variable indicate the resources required to produce one unit of each variable at a particular stage in the solution process.

c) The numbers in the rows show the relationship between each variable in the problem and each relevant resource of limited capacity (restrictions or constraints).

d) The economic values above each variable indicate their ef-

fect per unit on the objective function. In our bakery example these represent profit contributions per dozen. Only real
products have positive values. Slack variables, by definition,
have zero values since they represent fictitious products that
cost nothing to produce and have no market value.

e) There must be one slack variable for each restriction.

f) The number of real variables will depend on the nature of
the problem. The number can be equal to, less than, or more
than the number of equations. The simplex method can
handle very large numbers of real variables while the graphical method can handle only two.

g) The objective function must always include terms for slack
as well as real variables. By definition, the cost or contribution of any slack variable is always zero.

CHECKING YOUR COMPREHENSION

(Answers will be found at the end of the book)

Test your understanding of Section 4.2 by working the problem outlined below. Check your answers on p. 141.

Questions *1* to *4:* The Zeus Company

Review the information provided on pp. 28–29 concerning the
product mix decision for the Zeus Company.

1. How many of the following will be needed in framing this
   problem for solution? (a) Equations. (b) Slack variables.
   (c) Real variables.
2. Write the three equations which completely describe the relationships between all five variables and the restrictions.
3. Write the complete objective function.
4. Using Table 4.2 as a guide, develop a similar table for the
   Zeus problem.

4.3 DEVELOP INITIAL SOLUTION (*STEP* 2)

The computation procedure for the simplex method actually consists of hunting for better and better solutions until the optimal solution is discovered. Theoretically, the simplex procedure may be started at any basic solution, but for practical reasons the origin should be chosen as the initial solution since it is the easiest to visualize and to formulate.

The origin solution is represented by point A in Figure 3.6 (page 36). It is a technically feasible solution which, in the graphical analysis, was interpreted to mean that no cookie production takes place. Because this solution made no economic sense, the succeeding stages of the graphical analysis proceeded to move or change the product mix to those represented by other points on the feasibility polygon.

The interpretation of an origin solution in the simplex method is somewhat different from that in the graphical method. No real variables are produced. This means that all resources are idle insofar as iced and sugar cookies are concerned. Remember, however, that slack variables were defined as that portion of each resource not required for the production of real products. Therefore, the origin solution in the simplex method represents a solution that calls for the production of *slack variables only*. This makes no more economic sense than the origin solution in the graphical method, but it does provide a useful starting point from which better solutions may be developed.

In the bakery example, the origin solution indicates that no iced or sugar cookies are to be produced, and that all resources are to be allocated to the production of slack products (L, O, and M cookies). What quantities of each type are in the product mix at this point? Reference to Table 4.2 shows that 15 hours of direct labor are available. The only slack product that requires this resource is L cookies, so that the entire 15 hours may be devoted to their production. The first coefficient under Q_L in the table indicates that one hour of direct labor is required per dozen L cookies. The number of L cookies in the origin solution is, therefore, 15 dozen ($15 \div 1 = 15$). Similar reasoning applied to the other slack variables leads to the conclusion that the 120-dozen oven capacity should be used to produce 120 dozen O cookies, and that the 32 pounds of icing mix should be allocated to the production of 32 dozen M cookies. In summary, the product mix indicated by the origin solution in the simplex method would be

$$Q_I = 0, Q_S = 0, Q_L = 15, Q_O = 120, Q_M = 32.$$

For computation purposes the origin solution must be shown in tabular form, as in Table 4.3. Note that this table differs from Table 4.2 in two respects. First, the variables presently in the solution are shown on the left side of the table together with their economic values. The fact that these are all slack variables identifies this solution as that of the *origin*. Secondly, the title of the final column in the table has been changed from "Capacity" to "Production." Of course, the production of 15 dozen L cookies, 120 dozen O cookies, and 32 dozen M cookies actually represents idle capacity in the labor, oven, and icing-mix resources. The adoption of this fiction was necessary to meet the needs of the simplex computation framework. It is, however, an assumption that tries the patience of the reader who finds it difficult to describe "idle capacity" by any other term.

TABLE 4.3
Initial (Origin) Solution

Contribution Variables		20¢ Q_I	15¢ Q_S	0¢ Q_L	0¢ Q_O	0¢ Q_M	Cookie Production (in dozens)
0¢	Q_L	0.15	0.10	1	0	0	15
0¢	Q_O	1.0	1.0	0	1	0	120
0¢	Q_M	0.4	0.0	0	0	1	32

CHECKING YOUR COMPREHENSION

(Answers will be found at the end of the book)

See how well you understand Section 4.3 by answering the following questions. Check your answers against those provided on p. 142.

Questions 5 and 6: The Zeus Company

5. Using Table 4.3 as a guide, develop an origin solution for the Zeus problem.
6. What variables are "in solution" at the origin? Why are the coefficients in the columns representing slack variables normally zero or one at the origin?

4.4   EVALUATE AND SELECT VARIABLES FOR INTRODUCTION IN NEXT STAGE (*STEP 3*)

The key point to be kept in mind is that some mix of real and slack products is always being "produced" at any solution point. Thus, the introduction of a new variable is possible only if certain variables now in solution are given up or taken out of solution. We judge the wisdom of these proposed "new for old" trades by testing their effect on the objective function.

4.4.1   Evaluation of Variables

The column of figures for Q_I in Table 4.3 can be used to illustrate the evaluation process. First, we note that each dozen iced cookies brought into solution at this stage will give us a gross contribution of 20¢ per dozen. Next, the column of coefficients tells us how much of each variable currently "in solution" must be given up to make this possible. For example, each dozen iced cookies introduced will require taking out of solution 0.15 dozen L cookies (labor slack), 1.0 dozen O cookies, and 0.4 dozen M cookies. Is this a desirable trade? This question can be resolved by comparing the gross gain of the new product and the value of the variables given up.

1. Add: 1 dozen iced cookies. Gross gain (from contribution row in Table 4.3) $= 20¢$ per dozen.
2. Less: Value of products now in solution which must be given up to permit production of iced cookies.

   0.15 dozen L cookies @ $0¢$ per dozen $= 0¢$
   1.0 dozen O cookies @ $0¢$ per dozen $= 0¢$
   0.4 dozen M cookies @ $0¢$ per dozen $= 0¢$

   Loss of contribution $= \overline{0¢}$.
3. Net effect of proposed change in product mix:

   Gross gain $=$ $20¢$
   $-$ loss of contribution $=$ $0¢$
   Net effect per dozen $= \overline{+20¢}$.

Since our desired result is to maximize the dollar contribution, this appears to be a favorable trade.

A second alternative would be to introduce sugar cookies into the origin solution. We look to the data in the Q_s column of Table 4.3 and compute the net effect.

1. Gross gain if introduced $= 15¢$ per dozen.
2. Less: Value of variables (products) given up.

   0.10 L @ $0¢ = 0¢$
   1.0 O @ $0¢ = 0¢$
   0.0 M @ $0¢ = 0¢$

   Loss of contribution $= \overline{0¢}$.
3. Net effect $= 15¢ - 0¢ = +15¢$.

The above indicates that, at this stage in our analysis, bringing sugar cookies into the solution would have a favorable (positive) effect on the objective function of 15¢ for each dozen brought into the product mix.

4.4.2 Selection of Variable to Be Introduced

One criterion that may be used to select the alternative variable to be introduced at any stage of a simplex problem is that of *net effect per unit* on the measure of effectiveness or objective function. At this stage of the bakery example, this criterion would indicate that iced rather than sugar cookies should be brought into the product mix since they have a higher net contribution to profit and overhead per dozen.[7]

A second criterion that may be used in selecting from among the alternative variables which might be introduced is that of *net total effect* on the objective function. This is defined as the product of the net effect per unit and the number of units that could be introduced at that stage of the solution.[8] Since the net contributions per dozen have already been determined, it is now necessary to determine the number of dozens of iced and sugar cookies that might be introduced into the origin solution.

Our earlier computations showed that two variables (I and S cookies) not in the current (origin) solution have a favorable (positive in this case) net effect per unit. If it pays to trade one unit of these variables, we should bring as many as possible into the next (second) stage solution. The number of units which it

---

[7] This same conclusion was reached in the early stages of the graphical method analysis on the basis their contribution per dozen. The simplex method may seem like "the hard way" in this and other respects. Remember, however, that the simplex is also the only way of solving problems of this type that involve more than two variables.

[8] A significant advantage of the total effect criterion, especially when hand computation methods are being used, is that it should produce an optimum solution in the fewest total number of tables. In this particular problem it will require only three tables rather than the four needed by the per-unit criterion. Most computer programs use the net effect per unit.

is feasible to introduce is determined, as in our graphical example, by the restrictions. These computations can be made directly from the data in Table 4.3. Their meaning in a graphical context is illustrated by Figure 3.3 on p. 26.

A. If iced cookies are introduced (move from A toward B in Figure 3.3), the products to be displaced are defined by the coefficients in the Q_I column of Table 4.3.

1. L cookies (labor capacity) must be given up.
   a) Each dozen iced cookies displaces 0.15 dozen L cookies.
   b) The limit or restriction for L cookies is 15 dozen.
   c) The maximum number of iced cookies that may be introduced in terms of this restriction is, therefore, 100 dozen (point F in Figure 3.3).

2. O cookies (idle oven capacity) must also be given up.
   a) Each dozen iced cookies displaces 1.0 dozen O cookies.
   b) The restriction on O cookies is 120 dozen.
   c) The maximum number of iced cookies that may be introduced in terms of this restriction is 120 (point G in Figure 3.3).

3. In addition, M cookies (idle icing mix) must also be given up.
   a) The rate of substitution or exchange between iced cookies and M cookies is 1.0 to 0.4; each one dozen iced cookies displaces 0.4 dozen M cookies.
   b) The restriction on M cookies is 32 dozen.
   c) The limit on iced cookies corresponding to this restriction is 80 (point B in Figure 3.3).

4. The most limiting restriction for iced cookies is M cookies. Therefore the number of iced cookies that could be introduced at this stage is limited to 80 dozen. (Move to

point *B* in Figure 3.3. Solutions *F* and *G* are not technically feasible.)

5. The net total effect of bringing 80 dozen iced cookies into solution at this stage (point *B* in Figure 3.3) would be $80 \times 20\textcent = \$16.00$.

B. If sugar rather than iced cookies were to be introduced (move from *A* toward point *E* in Figure 3.3):

1. *L* cookies must be allocated to production of sugar cookies. The limit on sugar cookies would be 150 dozen $(15 \div .10)$.

2. *O* cookies must also be given up. Limit is 120 $(120 \div 1.0)$.

3. *M* cookies must also be given up. Limit—infinity $(32 \div 0)$, since sugar cookies require no icing mix.

4. Most limiting resource is *O* cookies. Therefore, only 120 dozen sugar cookies can be brought into solution at this stage.

5. Net total effect on objective function:
   120 dozen sugar cookies @ $15\textcent = \$18.00$.

C. *Conclusion:* Sugar cookies should be selected for introduction into the product mix. The total net effect of this variable at this stage of the analysis is greater ($\$18.00$) than that of iced cookies ($\$16.00$). A total of 120 dozen can be introduced in the next stage.

In our bakery example the net per-unit criterion suggests that iced cookies be introduced in the next stage. The computationally more involved criterion, net total effect, indicates that sugar cookies should be introduced since their total contribution is higher. Since we are doing hand calculations, our interest is in minimizing the number of iterations to reach the optimal solution. For this reason we select sugar cookies. Were a computer available to perform iterations, we would probably use the net per-unit criterion since the computer instructions for this method are easier to write.

CHECKING YOUR COMPREHENSION

(Answers will be found at the end of the book)

Test your understanding of *Step 3* in the simplex method by answering the following questions. Check your answers on p. 143.

Questions 7 and 8: The Zeus Company

7. Using your origin solution prepared for Question *5*, determine the net effect per unit for (a) standard, and (b) deluxe units. Which would you select for introduction?
8. Compute the net total effect for these two variables. On the basis of this criterion, which product should be introduced?

4.5 DEVELOP NEW TABLE OF EQUATIONS (*STEP 4*)

Once a variable has been selected for introduction, we proceed to develop another table of coefficients which will reflect the variables now in solution and their relationships. This is one of the most trying tasks in the simplex routine. We illustrate first a method which is helpful in understanding what is being done and why. Later, a more rapid computational method will be demonstrated. (See Appendix.)

4.5.1 Determine Variables Now in Solution

One of the key rules in linear programming is as follows: the number of variables in solution at any one time must be equal to the number of equations. In our bakery example there are three equations (rows in Table 4.3). This means that, if 120 dozen sugar cookies are introduced, (a) one of the variables in the origin solution must be displaced altogether, and (b) the "production" of slack products indicated in the other rows may be decreased.

Earlier computations for net total effect (see p. 61) indicated that O cookies (the slack variable for oven capacity) was the limiting factor should sugar cookies be introduced. This is the variable which will be displaced; that is, sugar cookies will replace O cookies in the second-stage solution.[9] This is shown in Table 4.4.

TABLE 4.4

Substitution of Variable for Second-Stage Solution

Contribution Variables	20¢ Q_I	15¢ Q_S	0¢ Q_L	0¢ Q_O	0¢ Q_M	Cookie Production (in dozens)
0¢ Q_L						3
15¢ Q_S						120
0¢ Q_M						32

Table 4.4 also indicates that only 3 dozen L and 32 dozen M cookies remain in the second-stage solution. These figures were computed as follows:

	In Origin Solution (Table 4.3)	Needed for 120 Dozen Q_S (from Table 4.3)	In Second Stage (Table 4.4)
L	15	120(.10)	15 − 12 = 3
O	120	120(1.0)	120 − 120 = 0 (out of solution)
M	32	120(0.0)	32 − 0 = 32

---

[9] See point E in Figure 3.3.

The number of L cookies in the second stage solution is reduced by the amount of labor needed to produce 120 dozen sugar cookies. Since no icing mix is required for sugar cookies, this slack variable remains unchanged.

In summary, the following guidelines may be used in determining which variables and what amounts of each appear in the next stage:

a) One variable is displaced from the previous solution by the new variable entering the next solution. The variable to be displaced is revealed in calculating how many of the new variables can be introduced. In the bakery example we determined that O cookies represented the limiting restriction in the previous (origin) solution and thus would be replaced in the next (second-stage) solution. This conclusion is reconfirmed by the calculation of the variables remaining in the next stage. No unused oven capacity (O cookies) remains in the second stage; therefore it is being displaced.

b) The production of other variables in the next solution is determined by subtracting the amount needed to produce the new variable from the quantity in the previous solution. For example, the column of coefficients under Q_s in Table 4.3 indicates that .10 lb. of L cookies (slack labor capacity) must be given up to produce one dozen sugar cookies. Since 15 dozen L's were in the previous (origin) solution, the amount in the next (second-stage) solution is $15 - 120(.10) = 3$ dozen.

4.5.2   Determine New Coefficients

What is needed to complete Table 4.4 is a revised set of coefficients which describe the new exchange rates between the variables now in solution (L, S, and M) and all variables in the problem. One method for computing these new coefficients follows:

a) Solve the column of coefficients for the *new* variable in terms of the variable being *displaced*. In our example, S is to replace O. From Table 4.3,

$$S = (.10)L + (1.0)O + (0)M.$$

Solving for O gives us

$$O = (1)S - (.10)L - (0)M. \tag{4.11}$$

Equation 4.11 represents the coefficients for the Q_0 column in the next stage.

b) Substitute this expression for the displaced variable wherever it is found in the "recipes" (columns) of the previous solution. In our bakery example the coefficients from the previous (origin) solution in Table 4.3 can be converted to the new set required in Table 4.4 by using Equation 4.11. For example,

$$
\begin{aligned}
I &= 0.15\,L + 1.0\,O + 0.4\,M \text{ (original coefficients)} \\
&= 0.15\,L + 1.0\,(S - 0.10\,L - 0\,M) + 0.4\,M \\
&= 0.05\,L + 1.0\,S + 0.4\,M
\end{aligned} \tag{4.12}
$$

$$
\begin{aligned}
L &= 1.0\,L + 0\,O + 0\,M \\
&= 1.0\,L + 0\,(S - 0.10\,L - 0\,M) + 0\,M \\
&= 1.0\,L + 0\,S + 0\,M
\end{aligned} \tag{4.13}
$$

$$
\begin{aligned}
S &= 0.10\,L + 1.0\,O + 0\,M \\
&= 0.10\,L + 1.0\,(S - 0.10\,L - 0\,M) + 0\,M \\
&= 0 \quad L + 1.0\,S + 0M
\end{aligned} \tag{4.14}
$$

$$
\begin{aligned}
M &= 0\,L + 0\,O + 1.0\,M \\
&= 0\,L + 0\,(S - 0.10\,L - 0\,M) + 1.0\,M \\
&= 0\,L + 0\,S + 1.0\,M
\end{aligned} \tag{4.15}
$$

The coefficients of Equations 4.11 through 4.15 may now be transferred to the appropriate columns of the second stage solution (Table 4.5). The solution described is that defined by point E in Figures 3.3 and 3.6. The meaning of the figures in Table 4.5 may be interpreted as follows:

1. L, S, and M are now in solution. The only real production

TABLE 4.5

Second-Stage Solution

Contribution Variables	20¢ Q_I	15¢ Q_S	0¢ Q_L	0¢ Q_0	0¢ Q_M	Cookie Production (in dozens)
0¢ Q_L	0.05	0	1	−0.10	0	3
15¢ Q_S	1	1	0	1	0	120
0¢ Q_M	0.4	0	0	0	1	32

is 120 dozen sugar cookies. The L and M "production" actually represents unused labor and icing mix.

2. The value of the objective function would be

$$0 \times 20¢ + 120 \times 15¢ + 3 \times 0¢ + 0 \times 0¢ + 32 \times 0¢ = \$18.00.$$

3. The effect of bringing other variables into solution at the next stage would be:

Iced Cookies: Reduce L by .05 per dozen,

Reduce S by 1.0 per dozen,

Reduce M by .4 per dozen.

O cookies: *Increase* L by .10 per dozen,[10]

Reduce S by 1.0 per dozen,

No effect on M (zero coefficient).

S, L, M: Already in the solution, so that adding would have no real effect. Note that the column of coefficients consists of zeros and a single one in each case. This is a standard format for any variable in solution.[11]

---

[10] Negative coefficients mean that resources or products will be *returned to* rather than given up in the product mix.

[11] The same 0 and 1 format applied to the slack variables in solution at the origin (see Table 4.3).

CHECKING YOUR COMPREHENSION

(Answers will be found at the end of the book)

See how well you understand the methods for developing a revised solution by working the problems outlined below. Check your answers against those found on p. 143.

Questions 9 to 12: The Zeus Company

9. Introduce 6,000 deluxe units into your second stage solution. Which variable will be displaced? What quantities of the other slack variables will remain in solution?
10. Develop the revised set of coefficients and show your table for the second-stage solution complete.
11. Compute the value of the objective function at this stage in the solution process.
12. Interpret the meaning of the coefficients in the following columns of your second-stage solution: standard, paint slack, and deluxe.

4.6 REPEAT STEPS 3 AND 4 (*STEP* 5)

Step 5 simply reminds us that linear programming is an iterative process, that is, the set of well-defined steps is repeated over and over until the calculations of *Step 3* show that no further improvement is possible.

4.6.1 *Steps 3 and 4 (Second Stage)*

The second-stage solution of Table 4.5 is a better solution than the origin of Table 4.3 because the objective function is $18.00 rather than zero. Is it the best possible or optimal solution? The only way to answer this question is to return once again to the tests described from *Step 3* in the simplex routine (see Section 4.4).

What variables might be introduced that are not now in solution? Both the I and O columns should be tested for net effect per unit. From Table 4.5,

I		O	
Gross Gain . . . . 20¢		Gross Gain . . . . 0¢	
Loss:		Loss:	
L . . . . . . 0.05 × 0¢ = 0¢		L . . . . . −0.10 × 0¢ = 0¢	
S . . . . . . 1.0 × 15¢ = 15¢		S . . . . . 1 × 15¢ = 15¢	
M . . . . . . 0.4 × 0¢ = 0¢		M . . . . . 0 × 0¢ = 0¢	
Total per dozen . . . 15¢		Total per dozen . . . 15¢	
Net change per dozen . . . . + 5¢		Net change per dozen . . . . −15¢	

Our conclusion is that iced cookies should be introduced since they have a favorable effect of 5¢ per dozen.[12] How many should be introduced? Once again we look to Table 4.5 and compute as follows:

	I	Production (dozen)	Limitation
L	0.05	3	3 ÷ 0.05 = 60
S	1	120	120 ÷ 1 = 120
M	0.4	32	32 ÷ 0.4 = 80

The L restriction is our limitation (see point D in Figure 3.3). In the next (third) stage solution 60 dozen iced cookies will displace L cookies from solution.

The other variables which will be in the third-stage solution can now be determined. Again, from Table 4.5:

	Production (second stage) − 60 Iced	=	Production (third stage)
L	3 − (60 × 0.05) =		0 (out of solution)
S	120 − (60 × 1) =		60
M	32 − (60 × 0.4) =		8

---

[12] The −15¢ evaluation for the oven slack variable is not surprising since this change would, in effect, return the solution to that of the origin.

Thus, the variables in the third-stage solution will be $Q_I = 60$, $Q_S = 60$, and $Q_M = 8$. Both O and L are now out of solution, that is, no excess capacity exists for the oven and labor resources.

The calculation of new coefficients proceeds as described in Section 4.5.2. First, the column for the variable entering solution is solved for the variable being displaced. In this case I displaces L. From Table 4.5,

$$I = 0.05(L) + 1(S) + 0.4(M),$$

and by solving for L, we find that

$$L = 20\,I - 20\,S - 8\,M. \tag{4.16}$$

This expression for L is then substituted wherever that factor appears in the columns of the second-stage solution of Table 4.5.

$$
\begin{aligned}
O &= -0.10\,L + 1.0\,S + 0\,M \text{ (old coefficients)} \\
&= -0.10(20\,I - 20\,S - 8\,M) + 1.0\,S + 0\,M \\
&= -2\,I + 2\,S + 0.8\,M + 1\,S + 0\,M \\
&= -2\,I + 3\,S + 0.8\,M \text{ (new coefficients)}. \qquad (4.17) \\
I &= 0.05(20\,I - 20\,S - 8\,M) + 1\,S + 0.4\,M \\
&= 1\,I - 1\,S - 0.4\,M + 1\,S + 0.4\,M \\
&= 1\,I + 0\,S + 0\,M. \qquad\qquad\qquad\qquad\qquad (4.18)
\end{aligned}
$$

The revised production data and new set of coefficients developed above may now be utilized to develop the third-stage solution as shown in Table 4.6.[13] This is the product mix represented by point D in Figures 3.3 and 3.6.

––––––––––

[13] The number of calculations required can be decreased if one remembers the 0 and 1 format for all variables in solution. The one is always found at the intersection of the row and column for the variable involved. In this sense the computation of new coefficients for I, S, and M is not necessary. The beginning student would be wise, however, to make at least one such calculation (as for I in 4.18) to double-check his calculations.

TABLE 4.6
Third-Stage Solution

Contribution Variables	20¢ Q_I	15¢ Q_S	0¢ Q_L	0¢ Q_0	0¢ Q_M	Cookie Production (in dozens)
20¢ Q_I	1	0	20	−2	0	60 iced
15¢ Q_S	0	1	−20	3	0	60 sugar
0¢ Q_M	0	0	−8	0.8	1	8 M

4.6.2 *Step 3* (Third Stage)

Although we know from our graphical illustration that the third-stage solution is optimal, the simplex procedure requires mathematical proof of this fact. For this purpose we return again to *Step 3* and calculate the net effect per dozen. These calculations, based on the data in Table 4.6, are shown in Table 4.7.

Since no variable has a favorable effect on the objective function (note net change per dozen), it is not necessary to carry the computations further.[14] The optimal product mix is therefore 60 dozen each of sugar and iced cookies. The corresponding value of the objective function is $21.00.

CHECKING YOUR COMPREHENSION
(Answers will be found at the end of the book)

Test your ability to carry a simplex problem to an optimal solution by performing the operations called for below. Check your answers against those provided on p. 144.

---

[14] It is considered good practice to test for net effect per unit on *all* variables in each iteration. The net for those variables currently in solution should always be zero as for *I, S,* and *M* in Table 4.8. This is another useful checking device for the beginning student when using hand calculations. On technical grounds one only needs to check those variables not in the current solution.

TABLE 4.7

Computation (in dollars)	Q_I	Q_S	Q_L	Q_O	Q_M
Gross gain per dozen ...	.20	.15	.00	.00	.00
Loss per dozen:					
Cookie I	$1 \times .20 = .20$	$0 \times .20 = .00$	$20 \times .20 = 4.00$	$-2 \times .20 = -.40$	$0 \times .20 = .00$
Cookie S	$0 \times .15 = .00$	$1 \times .15 = .15$	$-20 \times .15 = -3.00$	$3 \times .15 = .45$	$0 \times .15 = .00$
Cookie M	$0 \times .00 = .00$	$0 \times .00 = .00$	$-8 \times .00 = .00$	$.8 \times .00 = .00$	$1 \times .00 = .00$
Total loss per dozen	.20	.15	1.00	.05	
Net change (gain − loss) per dozen....	$.20 - .20 = .00$	$.15 - .15 = .00$	$.00 - 1.00 = -1.00$	$.00 - .05 = -.05$	$.00 - .00 = .00$

Questions *13* to *16:* The Zeus Company

13. Given your second-stage solution, which variable should now be introduced? How many units?

14. Which variable will be displaced? What quantities of the other variables will remain in the third-stage solution?

15. Develop the complete table for the third-stage solution.

16. Show that the third stage is optimal by testing all five problem variables for net effect per unit.

4.7 INTERPRETATION FOR IMPLEMENTATION (*STEP* 6)

The decision-maker is interested not only in the optimal solution to a linear programming problem, but also in additional information about the situation which the analyst's model can provide. Proper interpretation of the final simplex table is therefore an important final step in a linear programming analysis.

Which constraints are critical and what resources will not be fully utilized? Table 4.6 indicates, for example, that 8 dozen M cookies (really 8 pounds of icing mix) will remain on hand if the optimal mix is produced.[15]

We can use the data from Table 4.7 to provide additional information. For example, should the decision-maker wish to consider introducing oven slack, the opportunity cost of this change would be 5¢ for each unit. The coefficients in the Q_0 column indicate that such a change could be made by (a) increasing the mix by two dozen I cookies (-2 coefficient), (b) decreasing sugars by three dozen ($+3$ coefficient), and (c) reducing the amount of M slack by 0.8 dozen. Similarly, if there is some strong reason outside the programming model which

---

[15] If cookie mix had been included in the set of equations, the amount of this slack variable in the optimal solution would indicate the pounds of this resource not needed for production of real products.

suggests that labor slack is needed, the opportunity cost is $1.00 per hour.

4.8 SUMMARY

The simplex is the general method of linear programming. Any allocation problem that involves linearity and certainty can be solved through the use of this method.

Any linear programming method may be likened to an effective search procedure. The purpose of the search is to find that set of values for all variables that is technically feasible and that optimizes an appropriate objective function. The term "effective" is used in the sense that an optimal solution is obtained with the least possible computation effort.

The simplex computation procedure is more complicated than those of special methods such as the graphical and transportation methods because the absence of simplifying factors and assumptions makes it necessary to rely entirely on mathematical expressions.

The mathematics involved in the simplex method requires the use of equations rather than inequalities. To meet this requirement it is necessary to express unused or idle resources in the form of slack variables. In the bakery example, these slack variables represented fictitious products that were, by definition, produced with all resources not required by real products in the problem.

It is customary to start a simplex analysis at the origin solution since this is the simplest of the many possible solutions to formulate. Subsequent steps in the procedure involve bringing into the solution those variables that are shown to have a favorable effect on the measure of effectiveness. When all such favorable alternatives have been exhausted, the optimal solution has been reached and the analysis completed.

As with any quantitative method of analysis, the optimal solution to a simplex analysis is optimal only in the sense that all pertinent factors in the problem have been treated explicitly. Qualitative factors may require modification of this solution before a final decision can be made.

Most business problems that justify analysis within a simplex framework involve many variables and constraints. The use of a computer is therefore frequently required for economical computation. The most important steps in the problem solving process from a managerial viewpoint are, therefore, those of framing the problem and evaluating the results of the analysis.

4.9 REVIEW QUESTIONS

1. Why is the simplex method the general method of linear programming?

2. Explain why all relationships between variables and restrictions must be stated in equation form in this method.

3. What are slack variables? Why are they necessary in the simplex method? What effect do they have on the "answers" to problems analyzed by this method?

4. What is meant by a basic solution? The "origin" solution? Why is the latter normally used as the initial solution?

5. What do the coefficients within a simplex table represent? Why is it necessary to compute a new set for each table in the analysis?

6. What criteria may be used in determining which variable to bring into the solution at each stage of the computation procedure? What specific advantage does the total effect criterion have?

7. How does one know when an optimal solution has been reached?

4.10 EXERCISES

1. Work the bakery problem, but with the following modifications:

a) Include cookie mix (subscript C) in your set of four equations.

b) Use the *net effect per unit* criterion for determining which variable to introduce at each stage.

ANSWERS:

Stage	Points	In	Out	In Solution
#2	A to B	I	M	$I(80), L(3), O(40), C(40)$
#3	B to C	S	L	$I(80), S(30), O(10), C(22)$
#4	C to D	M	O	$I(60), S(60), M(8), C(24)$

Final Coefficients: For O, $(0.8M + 3S - 2I + 0.2C)$
For L, $(20I - 20S - 8M - 8C)$

2. The bakery manager is considering the introduction of a larger size sugar cookie ("Sugar King") into his product line. Several experimental batches have been produced and sold. Data collected during these runs indicate that (a) 1.2 pounds of cookie mix and 0.12 hours of labor are required per dozen, and (b) direct cost should be 65¢ per dozen. Limited market experience suggests that 95¢ per dozen would be an appropriate initial price.

a) Given these new facts and assuming no change in the other factors in the bakery problem:

(1) Write the set of linear equations which describes this three-product case.

(2) Develop an origin solution.

(3) Carry the problem to an optimum solution.

(4) Frame the problem using a three-dimensional display. Explain your analysis by means of this diagram.

b) Suppose that the baker decides: (a) to limit his initial production of "Sugar Kings" to 20 dozen per day, and

(b) to use the remaining resources for iced and regular sugar cookies. Determine the optimal product mix and expected contribution per day.

3. Solve the Lotanoiz Corporation problem stated in Section 3.8 using the simplex format.

4. Analyze the product mix decisions outlined in Section 3.8 for the Plummer Company by use of the simplex method.

5. A Junior Achievement group has been organized and has established the specifications and operations lists for three products (A, B, and C) which it feels the "company" could offer to the public in its product line. Both prices and direct costs have been established for each product. The same basic material and type of labor would be used for each product, but in different amounts.

	A	B	C
Material (square feet per unit)	3	5	4
Labor (minutes per unit)	6	3	7
Price per unit (in dollars)	5.50	5.00	5.25
Cost per unit (in dollars)	2.50	4.00	3.25

The purchasing agent has bought, paid for, and had 4200 square feet of material delivered. Because of school and other commitments, the group members have agreed to limit "hiring themselves" to no more than 4,200 minutes for direct labor operations.

Each product has its fans and considerable discussion has taken place as to whether one, two, or all three products should be produced. They do agree, however, that their objective is to maximize profits.

They have turned to you, as a person with some knowledge of linear programming, to assist them in determining their product mix. Apparently no sales restrictions need to be considered since, in the words of the young president, "If we get in a jam, our parents will always help us out."

a) Set up and solve using the simplex format.

b) Interpret your solution for the J. A. group.

c) Could this problem also be solved graphically?

6. The Gypsum Company wishes to produce three products (*A, B,* and *C*) so as to realize the maximum total profit from the sale of the products. Each product is made in two processes (I and II). It takes 8 hours in Process I and 5 hours in Process II to manufacture one *A*. It requires 9 hours in Process I and 3 hours in Process II to manufacture one product *B*. Also one product *C* requires 4 hours in Process I and 7 hours in Process II.

Process I can handle 140 hours of work and Process II can take 86 hours of work in the schedule period. The profit is $13 for Product *A*, $9 for Product *B*, and $6 for Product *C*.

a) What are the constraint inequalities?

b) Construct the objective function.

c) How many products of the three possibilities will appear in your optimal solution?

d) Develop an initial solution.

e) Determine which product should be brought into the next stage.

f) Develop the table for the second stage.

g) Carry the problem to an optimal solution.

7. "I need our product mix decision for next period right away," the boss roared at 10:30 A.M. this morning. "Pete's gone for the day, Mr. Bigsome, but here's a rough simplex table on his desk. Maybe this is his optimal solution," you suggested cautiously. After adjusting his glasses several times and then turning a deep purple, the boss blasted again: "I don't understand it! Unless you can explain it to me by 11:45 today, I'm going to

let Pete start confusing some other company." Pete needs the job and a friend—please help.

	$0 S	$0 F	$0 W	$0 P	$20 A	$30 B	$25 C	
$30 B	0.63	−0.34	0	−0.12	0	1	0	3,900
$20 A	−0.16	0.88	0	−0.16	1	0	0	15,250
$ 0 W	0.44	−1.82	1	−3.71	0	0	0	10,440
$25 C	−0.14	−0.24	0	0.50	0	0	1	8,620

a) "Is it his optimal solution? How do you know?"

b) "I told him to maximize R.O.I. for the period. Has he followed my instructions? How much money will we make?"

c) "What does this solution tell me about our output of products A, B, and C? Will our stamping, forming, welding, and plating departments all be operating at capacity?"

d) "Pete's mentioned 'slack variables' once or twice. Where are they here and what do they mean?"

e) "I understand that Rick, the college boy we put in as foreman of the stamping department last week, is having his troubles with absenteeism, so his capacity may be a little less than Pete figured on. Can you give me an idea of how much profit we'll lose for every hour of stamping capacity he can't achieve? Would there be corresponding adjustments needed in our product mix and/or departmental workloads?"

8. The Carter Company currently enjoys a strong demand for its Standard Product so that, in effect, it can be sold in unlimited quantities at the list price of $1.55 per unit. However, the long-term market trend appears to be toward more "trading up" among buyers. As a consequence, the initial product and process specifications have just been completed for a new, deluxe model which would be priced initially at $1.80 per unit.

The firm is now planning its weekly output for the next quarterly planning period. Because the company does not wish to expand its investment in plant and equipment, no changes in capacity are contemplated during this period. However, an arrangement has just been made with a local foundry to provide additional castings, if needed, during the period.

There has been some disagreement over the "correct" product mix for the quarter. While he agrees that it is not critical, the sales manager would like to have some production of the deluxe items. The production manager is being pressed by the new foundry supplier for a preliminary estimate of volume for the quarter.

Late yesterday, agreement was reached that an analyst would be asked to evaluate the problem and to present his findings this morning. The following ground rules for the analysis were established:

1. Because profit conditions were so favorable, the mix must maximize return on investment over the quarter.
2. If justified on the above basis, limited production of up to as many as 1500 units of the deluxe item could be produced per week.

The relevant cost estimates, process times, and planned capacities are shown below.

	Standard	Deluxe	Capacity Available
Costs (dollars per unit):			
Purchased casting	.60	.70	
Casting operation*	.40	.60	
Machining operation	.25	.15	
Assembling operation	.30	.25	
Time (minutes per week):			
Casting operation	5	10	5,000
Machining operation	8	4	8,000
Assembling operation	4	3	6,000

* Exclusive of fixed overhead costs.

REQUIRED:

Assume you are the analyst. Your work should demonstrate your knowledge of the following:

Problem Formulation

a) Set up the problem for solution by linear programming and develop an initial solution. Explain each variable and constraint.

b) Develop an objective function.

Interpretive Skills

c) Is the objective function of your model consistent with that stated by management? How would the fixed overhead costs in our own casting department be treated in the analysis?

d) Would your approach to (*a*) above have been different if the agreement had been that *exactly* 1500 deluxe units *must* be produced next quarter?

e) If both standard and deluxe units are to be produced, it is quite likely that some downtime will be necessary in the machining department to change machinery over from one product to another. Have you included, or could you include this fact in your analysis?

f) What specific kinds of information would you hope to be able to provide for management from the optimal solution?

Manipulative Skills

g) Given your initial solution in (*a*), carry the problem through to an optimal solution. Show specifically that your solution yields the kinds of information you noted in answering question (*f*).

5 | The Transportation Method

5.1 GENERAL NATURE OF THE METHOD

Complex allocation problems having certain characteristics may be solved by a special, highly simplified version of the simplex method referred to as the transportation, distribution, or stepping-stone method of linear programming. It is especially appropriate for source-to-destination situations such as the transportation of goods from plants to distribution facilities. The same solution framework, however, may be applied to a wide variety of problems. Thus the characteristics of the problem itself rather than its institutional or functional setting determine whether or not this method is applicable.

The key characteristic of problems for which the method is suited is *homogeneity*. All rates of substitution between variables must be *one-to-one*. Such a condition was illustrated in the bakery example by the relationship between the real products and the oven resource; one dozen iced cookies could be substituted for a dozen sugar cookies in terms of oven capacity, and vice versa. Since the other rates of substitution in the product mix example were not one-to-one, the key characteristic of the transportation method was not met by that problem.

Like all linear programming methods, the transportation method is an iterative process. After an initial solution has been formulated, the computational procedure provides an effective method for developing improved solutions until the optimum is reached. The nature and meaning of the steps in this procedure as well as the homogeneity assumption will be demonstrated in the following sample problem.

THE McCLAIN CONSTRUCTION COMPANY

The McClain Company will have four major construction projects under way next month, an unusually high level of activity for the firm. As a consequence, the volume of materials that must be moved from the local supply yard exceeds the capacity of the company's truck fleet. Rather than purchase additional trucks and hire new drivers, the company management has decided to contract with local haulers for as much of the total hauling task as is justified on an economic basis.

The expected hauling requirements, expressed in truckloads, for the construction sites during the next month are as follows:

Site	Requirements (in loads)
Number 1................	60
Number 2................	90
Number 3................	75
Number 4................	65
Total:	290

Three local trucking firms have submitted bids indicating their price per load from the local supply yard to each site and the maximum number of loads for which they would be willing to contract. This information is summarized as follows:

Site	Cost per Load (dollars)		
	Firm A	Firm B	Firm C
Number 1	6	3	6
Number 2	6	6	5
Number 3	7	4	4
Number 4	7	5	3
Maximum Capacity (loads)	100	80	70

The capacity of the McClain Company's truck fleet for the same period is 60 loads. Expected costs are as follows:

Site	Cost per Load— McClain Co.
Number 1...............	$5
Number 2...............	3
Number 3...............	5
Number 4...............	6

Since substantial differences exist in the relative costs of the various assignments that might be made, the McClain Company must now decide which hauling requirements will be assigned to company trucks and which to each of the trucking firms.

5.2 FRAME THE PROBLEM (*STEP 1*)

As in other linear programming methods, the data relevant to the problem must first be organized in a logical fashion. The matrix of a transportation analysis serves the same basic purpose as the display of the graphical method and the tables of coefficients in the simplex format. All frame the decision variables in such a manner that alternatives can be identified, evaluated, and the search for improved solutions facilitated.

The *certainty* assumptions will be met if we accept the single numbers which represent requirements and capacities as realistic forecasts. The assumption of *linearity* is reflected in the cost structure of the problem, that is, the variable cost per load is independent of the number of loads assigned to each source. Finally, the *homogeneity* assumption in this problem means that one "load" is the same whether it is hauled in company or contractor trucks.

5.2.1 Determination of Rim Requirements

The constraints in a transportation matrix are normally referred to as *rim requirements*. In the McClain example, the total hauling capacity (sources) available is the sum of the individual capacities for the company fleet plus the various suppliers:

$$60 + 100 + 80 + 70 = 310 \text{ loads capacity.} \qquad (5.1)$$

Total material requirements for the various construction sites (destinations) may also be expressed in equation form:

$$60 + 90 + 75 + 65 = 290 \text{ loads required.} \qquad (5.2)$$

Comparison of Equations 5.1 and 5.2 indicates that total capacity exceeds requirements by 20 loads for the period.

The transportation method, like the simplex, requires the use of equalities, so that slack variables must be used to represent idle or unused resources. One way of doing this in the McClain problem would be to create an artificial site requiring 20 loads of hauling capacity.[1] Addition of this slack site requirement results in the following:

$$60 + 90 + 75 + 65 + 20 = 310 \text{ load requirement.} \quad (5.3)$$

Equations 5.1 and 5.3 may now be entered as the rim requirements, as shown in Table 5.1.

---

[1] Occasionally, problems will be encountered where requirements exceed capacity; in such cases, slack would represent unfilled orders.

TABLE 5.1

	Sources of Hauling Capacity				
	Firm				Material
Site	M	A	B	C	Requirements
No. 1	$5	$6	$3	$6	60
No. 2	$3	$6	$6	$5	90
No. 3	$5	$7	$4	$4	75
No. 4	$6	$7	$5	$3	65
Slack	$0	$0	$0	$0	20
Hauling Capacity	60	100	80	70	310

5.2.2 Enter Cell Values

The 20 cells within Table 5.1 represent the various source-to-destination assignments or allocations that are feasible. For example, the 100-load capacity of Firm A may be used, in whole or in part, to meet the needs of any of the four sites. A portion of it (up to 20 units) could also be allocated to meet the slack requirement.[2] Any combination of assignments for Firm A would be acceptable as long as the total equaled exactly 100 units.

---

[2] An allocation of 20 units of Firm A's capacity to the slack site would mean, in effect, that only 80 units would be contracted for.

Similarly, the 60-unit requirement of Site No. 1 may be met by any combination of assignments among the various hauling resources as long as the total equals 60.

Each of these alternatives has certain economic values associated with it. These values (normally costs or profits) are conventionally noted in the upper left-hand corner of each cell. The entries in Table 5.1, for example, show the costs associated with assigning each capacity to each requirement. Thus the cost for hauling to Site No. 1 will be $5 by company trucks, $6 by Firm A, and so forth. By definition, the value (cost in our example) of any slack variable is zero.[3]

5.2.3 Selection of Objective Function

As in the graphical and simplex methods, the "best" or optimal solution to a transportation problem (a) is feasible, that is, it satisfies all rim requirements; and (b) maximizes or minimizes an appropriate objective function. Thus the final task in framing the problem is to state an explicit objective function. If one assumes that the quality of the service provided by the various truck fleets is equal, the minimization of total hauling costs for the month would be a reasonable criterion.[4]

$$\text{Total Hauling Cost} = \quad \text{Cost for Site No. 1}$$
$$+ \text{ Cost for Site No. 2}$$
$$+ \text{ Cost for Site No. 3}$$
$$+ \text{ Cost for Site No. 4}$$
$$+ \text{ Cost for slack site}$$

---

[3] Remember that slack is used to make the problem computationally feasible and simply represents unused resources.

[4] Technically, the assumptions relative to service are not required. If some explicit cost could be assigned to poor service, this cost could be added to the prices within each cell and a pure-cost-minimization criterion adopted.

Since the cost at each site is a function of the trucks utilized and how many loads are assigned to each, the complete objective function is

$$
\begin{aligned}
\text{T.H.C.} = \quad & \$5\,Q_{1M} + \$6\,Q_{1A} + \$3\,Q_{1B} + \$6\,Q_{1C} \\
& + \$3\,Q_{2M} + \$6\,Q_{2A} + \$6\,Q_{2B} + \$5\,Q_{2C} \\
& + \$5\,Q_{3M} + \$7\,Q_{3A} + \$4\,Q_{3B} + \$4\,Q_{3C} \\
& + \$6\,Q_{4M} + \$7\,Q_{4A} + \$5\,Q_{4B} + \$3\,Q_{4C} \\
& + \$0\,Q_{SM} + \$0\,Q_{SA} + \$0\,Q_{SB} + \$0\,Q_{SC}
\end{aligned}
$$

Because this is a long expression, the objective function is ordinarily expressed in the form of a summation, namely,

$$
\text{T.H.C.} = \Sigma C_{ij} \times Q_{ij},
$$

where

$$
i = 1, 2, 3, 4, S, \text{ and}
$$
$$
j = M, A, B, C
$$

CHECKING YOUR COMPREHENSION

(Answers will be found at the end of the book)

Check your understanding of Section 5.2. (Framing the Problem) by developing the matrix for solution of the Uni-Product Company problem outlined below. Check your answers on p. 146.

THE UNI-PRODUCT COMPANY

The Uni-Product Company manufactures a single product in four plants located through the Midwest. Completed products can be shipped from each of the plants to any of the four company warehouses.

The shipments required by each warehouse over the next quarter are as follows:

Warehouse A—65 carloads

"   B—40 carloads

"   C—60 carloads

"   D—55 carloads

Planned manufacturing capacity (in carloads) for each plant during the next quarter is as follows:

Plant No. 1—45 carloads

"   "   2—65 carloads

"   "   3—45 carloads

"   "   4—75 carloads

The company management wishes to minimize the total transportation cost of shipping from the company plants to warehouses. The traffic manager has provided the following schedule of anticipated transportation costs:

	Cost per Carload from Plant Number			
	1	*2*	*3*	*4*
To warehouse:				
A	$ 8	$5	$4	$6
B	8	6	7	5
C	10	7	5	3
D	6	5	7	3

Questions 1 to 3: Uni-Product Company

1. Will a slack warehouse or plant be required? Why?
2. Construct the matrix for solution by the transportation method (plants across top of matrix).
3. Write the objective function for this analysis.

5.3 DEVELOP AN INITIAL SOLUTION (*STEP* 2)

In the transportation method, unlike the simplex, the initial solution need not be the origin solution. The only requirement of an initial solution in the transportation method is that it be technically feasible, that is, it must not violate any of the rim requirements. This means that the amount of subsequent computational work is, in part, a result of the starting position selected.

There are several standard procedures for developing initial solutions. Two appropriate ones for the beginning student are the Northwest Corner Rule and the North-to-South Row Rule, a simple inspection method. Other more sophisticated methods can be used to advantage once the basic structure of the tranportation method has been mastered.

5.3.1 Inspection Method for Initial Solution

The inspection method used here is a simple one which will be referred to as the North-to-South Row Rule. This rule operates as follows:

a) Starting with the first or north row, fill the requirements of each row in order, using the lowest cost assignment available within the limits imposed by previous allocations.

b) After all row requirements have been met, add across each row and down each column to insure that all rim requirements have been met.

The North-to-South Row Rule will be applied to the McClain problem in the remainder of this section.

Inspection of Table 5.2 shows that the lowest cost capacity for the 60-load requirement at Site No. 1 is Firm B. This firm has 80 loads available; therefore 60 loads are assigned as shown in cell 1–B. Only 20 loads of Firm B's capacity are now available to other sites.

For Site No. 2 the McClain fleet represents the lowest cost resource, but only 60 loads are available (Table 5.2). The additional 30 loads must therefore be secured from Firm C, which represents the next lowest cost capacity. Once these assignments have been recorded, the requirements for both Sites No. 1 and No. 2 have been met.

TABLE 5.2

Sources of Hauling Capacity

| Site | Firm | | | | *Material Requirements* |
	M	*A*	*B*	*C*	
No. 1	$5	$6	$3 / 60	$6	60
No. 2	$3 / 60	$6	$6	$5 / 30	90
—					—
Hauling Capacity	60	100	80	70	310

Table 5.3 shows two lowest cost sources for Site No. 3—Firms B and C. However, a portion of their capacities have already been allocated. Also, the McClain fleet has been fully assigned. Therefore, the most economical assignment which can be made at this point is the one shown in Table 5.3.[5]

---

[5] A feasible alternative would be to secure all 75 loads from Firm A. Such an allocation would not, however, follow our rule of using the lowest cost assignment available.

TABLE 5.3

Initial Solution: North to South Row Rule

Sources of Hauling Capacity

| | | Firm | | | Material |
Site	M	A	B	C	Requirements
No. 1	$5	$6	$3 / 60	$6	60
No. 2	$3 / 60	$6	$6	$5 / 30	90
No. 3	$5	$7 / 15	$4 / 20	$4 / 40	75
No. 4	$6	$7 / 65	$5	$3	65
Slack	$0	$0 / 20	$0	$0	20
Hauling Capacity	60	100	80	70	310

The initial solution may now be completed by assigning 65 loads of hauling capacity to Site No. 4 and 20 loads to the slack site. Table 5.3 shows that, as a result of previous allocations, it is necessary to select Firm A even though it has the highest cost. Further analysis in later stages will enable adjustments in this and other assignments to be made in the event that they are warranted.

The meaning of the initial solution in Table 5.3 may be interpreted as follows:

1. Company trucks will haul 60 loads to Site No. 2.

2. Only 80 loads of the 100 load capacity offered by Firm A will be contracted for. Of the units hired, 15 will haul to Site No. 3 and 65 to Site No. 4.

3. Sixty loads of Firm B's capacity will be assigned to Site No. 1 and 20 to Site No. 3.

4. Thirty loads of Firm C's capacity will be assigned to Site No. 2 and 40 to Site No. 3.

This solution is feasible in the sense that none of the rim requirements has been violated. This is the only necessary condition for an initial solution; it need not make much economic sense. The North-to-South Row Rule for initial solutions did make use of cost data, but on a row-by-row rather than an overall basis.

The cost of this solution (objective function) may be determined by summing the costs for the various sites:

Site No. 1: 3×60 $= \$ \quad 180$
Site No. 2: $3 \times 60 + \$5 \times 30$ $= \quad 330$
Site No. 3: $7 \times 15 + \$4 \times 20 + \$4 \times 40 = \quad 345$
Site No. 4: 7×65 $= \quad 455$
Total Cost (Initial Solution) $\overline{\$1,310}$

5.3.2 The Northwest Corner Rule for Initial Solution

There is nothing special about the northwest corner of a matrix. This so-called "rule" is simply a convenient convention which may be stated as follows:

a) Starting at the upper left hand or northwest corner, fill the requirements of each row, in order, from the columns, in order.

b) Check for compliance with rim requirements.

This rule has been applied to the McClain problem in Table 5.4.

TABLE 5.4

Initial Solution: Northwest Corner Method

	Sources of Hauling Capacity				
	Firm				*Material*
Site	*M*	*A*	*B*	*C*	*Requirements*
No. 1	60				60
No. 2		90			90
No. 3		10	65		75
No. 4			15	50	65
Slack				20	20
Hauling Capacity	60	100	80	70	310

The 60-load requirement of the first row is met with the capacity of the first (M) column. Move down to the second row. This requirement is met with 90 units from the second (A) column. The remaining 10 units are applied toward the 75-load requirement of the third row. An additional 65 units must be secured from the third (B) column to fill Row 3. The 15 units left in Column B are applied to Row 4. The capacity of Column C is then used to meet the remaining requirement of Row 4 and the slack-site row.[6] Adding rows and columns indicates that this is a feasible solution.

---

[6] It is unusual when only one column is needed to fill one row as in cell 1-M. When this occurs, it is a sign of degeneracy, a condition to be discussed in the next section.

Initial solutions based upon the Northwest Corner method can always be recognized by their stair-step appearance. Because the method is concerned exclusively with developing this pattern, it ignores costs. For example, the McClain trucks would have been assigned to Site No. 1 no matter what cost appeared in cell 1–M. The cost data were omitted from the cells of Table 5.4 to illustrate this point.

When properly applied, both the North to South Row inspection method and the Northwest Corner Rule will produce feasible initial solutions. Because the latter ignores costs, more computations are usually required to optimize the problem.[7] Both are acceptable methods, so that the basis for selecting between them is essentially one of personal preference.

5.4   TEST THE SOLUTION FOR DEGENERACY (*STEP* 3)

Degeneracy is a special condition which can arise in any type of linear programming problem. Since it is most likely to occur even in elementary problems when the transportation method is used, the beginning student should be able to (a) recognize the condition, and (b) devise measures for dealing with it.

Cells within which assignments have been made represent the variables currently in a particular solution. For example, in the initial solution of Table 5.3, cells 1–B, 2–M and all others with entries are used cells. The unused cells (1–M, 2–A, . . .) are those variables in the problem which are not yet in the solution.

The computation procedure can be carried out only if the number of used cells within the matrix conforms to the Rim Minus One Rule.

Used Cells = Number of Rows + Number of

Columns − 1   (5.4)

---

[7] The cost of the initial NW Corner solution is $1,395 versus $1,310 for the inspection solution. The more "fat" in the solution, the more iterations are required.

There are five rows and four columns in the McClain problem. Inspection of Table 5.3 reveals that there are eight used cells. This solution is ready for *Step 4*. The initial solution of Table 5.4 is degenerate since this matrix contains only seven used cells. The measures which must be taken on this matrix will be more readily understood when they are discussed in Section 5.9.

CHECKING YOUR COMPREHENSION

(Answers will be found at the end of the book)

Check your understanding of Sections 5.3 and 5.4 by answering the following questions based on the Uni-Product problem. Check your answers on p. 147.

Questions 4 to 9: The Uni-Product Company

4. Develop an initial solution using the North to South Row Rule.
5. Test for degeneracy by applying the Rim Minus One Rule.
6. Interpret the solution, that is, which plants will ship what quantities to which warehouses?
7. Determine the total cost of your initial solution.
8. Develop an initial solution using the Northwest Corner Rule.
9. Test for degeneracy.

5.5 EVALUATE UNUSED CELLS (*STEP 4*)

The evaluation process of *Step 4* tests each unused cell for its effect on the objective function. If an unused cell has a favorable effect (can reduce cost in this case), it is brought into the solution (becomes a used cell). Each cell handled in this fashion must displace a former used cell in order to comply with the

Rim Minus One Rule. Two alternative procedures for evaluating unused cells will be presented, namely, the Stepping-Stone and MODI methods.

5.5.1   The Stepping-Stone Method

What would happen if one load were tentatively assigned to cell 2–B in Table 5.5? Note that such an assignment would result in violations of the rim requirements for both Site 2 and Firm B. This means that, if cell 2–B is to be utilized, compensating adjustments must be made in other assignments. For example, if the McClain fleet were to haul 59 rather than 60 loads to

TABLE 5.5

	Sources of Hauling Capacity				
	Firm				*Material*
Site	*M*	*A*	*B*	*C*	*Requirements*
No. 1			60		
No. 2	60		1	30	90
No. 3			20		
No. 4					
Slack					
Hauling Capacity			80		

Site No. 2, the change would become feasible $(59 + 1 + 30 = 90)$. An alternative would be to decrease the loads destined for Site No. 2 which are carried by the trucks of Firm C $(60 + 1 + 29 = 90)$. To make the proposed change feasible in terms of Firm B, the number of loads to be hauled to Site No. 1 might be decreased to 59 $(59 + 1 + 20 = 80)$, or the loads to Site No. 3 decreased by 1 $(60 + 1 + 19 = 80)$.

For reasons that will become apparent later, suppose that the decision is made to decrease cell 2–C to 29 and cell 3–B to 19 loads. Has the full solution now been restored to a state of technical feasibility? An inspection of Table 5.6 suggests that it has not. Specifically, the change has produced second-order diffi-

TABLE 5.6

Sources of Hauling Capacity

Site	Firm M	A	B	C	Material Requirements
No. 1			60		60
No. 2	60		1	29	90
No. 3		15	19	41	75
No. 4		65			65
Slack		20			20
Hauling Capacity	60	100	80	70	310

culties (side effects) within Row 3 and Column C. Site No. 3 now has only 74 loads assigned, rather than the required 75, and Firm C has been reduced to 69 loads. The only appropriate remedy would be to allocate one additional load to cell 3–C (41 loads). Once this change has been made the solution is again feasible. Thus the first step in evaluating unused cells by the Stepping-Stone method is to find the chain of assignment changes (evaluation route) necessary to make the proposal consistent with the rim requirements.

When these changes have been determined, we evaluate their effect on the objective function (cost consequences in this problem). The net results of the cell 2–B proposal are summarized as follows:

	B	C
2	$6 +1 load	$5 −1 load
3	$4 −1 load	$4 +1 load

One load was added to cell 2–B (0 → 1) and to cell 3–C (40 → 41). These changes would add $10 ($6 + $4) to the total hauling cost. At the same time, units were tentatively subtracted from cell 2–C (30 → 29) and from cell 3–B (20 → 19), with corresponding decrease in hauling cost of $9 ($5 + $4). Thus the net economic effect of these changes would be to increase the total cost of the solution by $1 for each load shifted in this manner. Since the objective is to reduce total hauling cost, the introduction of cell 2–B into the solution would not represent an improvement in the assignment mix.

The mechanics of determining evaluation routes is facilitated by following these rules:

1. Only one unused cell may be evaluated at a time.

2. Other than the unused cell being evaluated, only used cells may be part of an evaluation route.[8]
3. There should always be only one unique route for each cell.[9]

Generally, it is least difficult to visualize those routes for which all adjustments in assignments can be made within four adjacent cells, as for cell 2–B in the sample problem. Routes forming a rectangle, three corners of which are used cells, are also easy to identify. Some routes, however, involve more than four cells and appear to be geometrical equivalents of the "calf path."

An additional illustration should be helpful in developing the meaning of these rules. From Table 5.3 the evaluation of cell 1–C would proceed as follows: The addition of one load to this cell would require that one unit be subtracted from a used cell both in Row 1 and in Column C. The latter adjustment might be made in either cell 2–C or 3–C, while the former can be made only in cell 1–B since this is the only used cell in Row 1. Reduction of cell 1–B by one unit means that one load must now be added to some used cell in Column B. Cell 3–B represents the only possibility. The addition of one unit to cell 3–B would then require subtraction of one unit from some used cell in Row 3, either 3–A or 3–C. Using the latter will complete the cycle in that this will also satisfy the requirement that one unit be deducted from a used cell in Column C. The value of cell 1–C would be $+ \$3$ $(+ 6 - 3 + 4 - 4)$. This, of course, is not a favorable move.

Other cells that are relatively easy to evaluate because the

---

[8] Early descriptions of this method referred to unused cells as "water" and to used cells as "stones." Thus, only "stones" could be used in evaluating "water" cells; hence the term "Stepping-Stone method" arose.

[9] As long as the number of used cells equals rim minus one, this will be true. When two or more feasible routes are found, more assignments have been made than necessary, and the solution can be simplified. Where no route is available, degeneracy is indicated.

evaluation route follows the format of three filled corners of a rectangle are indicated here:

Unused Cell	Route	Economic Effect
3–M	3–M, 3–C, 2–C, 2–M	+$3 per unit
S–C	S–C, S–A, 3–A, 3–C	+$3 per unit
S–B	S–B, S–A, 3–A, 3–B	+$3 per unit
4–B	4–B, 4–A, 3–A, 3–B	+$1 per unit
2–A	2–A, 2–C, 3–C, 3–A	−$2 per unit
4–C	4–C, 4–A, 3–A, 3–C	−$1 per unit

TABLE 5.7

Cell Evaluations: First Stage Solution

	Sources of Hauling Capacity				
	Firm				Material Requirements
Site	M	A	B	C	
No. 1	$5 +4	$6 0	$3 / 60	$6 +3	60
No. 2	$3 / 60	$6 (−2)	$6 +1	$5 / 30	90
No. 3	$5 +3	$7 / 15	$4 / 20	$4 / 40	75
No. 4	$6 +4	$7 / 65	$5 +1	$3 (−1)	65
Slack	$0 +5	$0 / 20	$0 +3	$0 +3	20
Hauling Capacity	60	100	80	70	310

The evaluation routes for the other cells are somewhat more difficult. The route for cell 1–M, for example, involves 1–M, 1–B, 3–B, 3–C, 2–C, and 2–M, and has an economic effect of +$4. Evaluation of cell S–M involves S–M, 2–M, 2–C, 3–C, 3–A, and S–A. Each unit added to this cell will increase the total cost of the assignment mix by $5. Obviously, this transfer does not represent a favorable change.

For convenience and ease of analysis it is conventional to note the net economic effect for each unused cell within the cell, as shown in Table 5.7. Note that only two cells (2–A and 4–C) have negative values. These represent opportunities to decrease the total cost of the hauling problem.[10]

CHECKING YOUR COMPREHENSION

(Answers will be found at the end of the book)

Evaluate your grasp of the Stepping-Stone method presented in Section 5.5.1 by answering the questions which follow. Answers are provided on p. 147.

Questions 10 and 11: The Uni-Product Company

10. Use the Stepping-Stone method to evaluate the following unused cells in your initial solution from Question 4. List the route and evaluation for each cell.

a) C–1	*d*) B–2
b) Slack − 2	*e*) A–1
c) A–4	*f*) B–1.

---

[10] Since this is a cost minimization problem, a positive net economic effect represents increased total cost. For profit maximization problems, where the economic data within each cell represent profits rather than costs, positive cell values would represent favorable changes in the measure of effectiveness.

11. Evaluate the remaining unused cells.

5.5.2 The MODI Method for Evaluating Unused Cells

The Modified Distribution or MODI Method is an alternative to the Stepping-Stone procedure for evaluating unused cells. It is somewhat more expedient and proceeds as follows:

a) The first row is arbitrarily assigned a zero coefficient.
b) This coefficient together with the cost or profit entries in the *used* cells are utilized to determine coefficients for all other rows and the columns.
c) Each *unused* cell is evaluated by subtracting the sum of the corresponding row and column coefficients from the cell entry.

Steps 1 and 2 of the MODI Method for evaluating unused cells are applied in Table 5.8 to the initial solution of Table 5.3. Only the relevant portion of the matrix (cost entries in used cells) is shown. The magnitude of the used cell assignments and the cost entries in unused cells are omitted since they are not relevant to these steps.

First, a coefficient of zero is arbitrarily assigned to Row 1.[11] Next, the other row and column coefficients are determined using Equation 5.5:

$$R_i + K_j = C_{ij}, \qquad (5.5)$$

where

$R_i =$ coefficient of the *i*th row,
$K_j =$ coefficient of the *j*th column, and
$C_{ij} =$ cost or profit entry in used cell *ij*.

---

[11] Actually the arbitrary zero can be assigned to any row or any column. The first-row convention will be used here.

TABLE 5.8

Determination of Row and Column Coefficients:
MODI Method

R_i ↓	$K_M =$	$K_A =$	$K_B = 3$	$K_C =$	←K_j
$R_1 = 0$			3		
$R_2 =$	3			5	
$R_3 = 1$		7	4	4	
$R_4 =$		7			
$R_S =$	0				

For example, the entry in cell 1–B is equal to the sum of the coefficients for Row 1 and Column B $(R_1 + K_B = C_{1B})$. Since both R_1 and C_{1B} are known, the equation can be solved for the unknown column coefficient:

$$K_B = C_{1B} - R_1 = 3 - 0 = 3.$$

Now this column coefficient can be used, together with the cell entry in 3–B, to determine the coefficient of Row 3:

$$R_3 = C_{3B} - K_B = 4 - 3 = 1.$$

The remaining computations would be as follows:[12]

---

[12] The reader should follow these computations using Table 5.8, and enter each coefficient in the table as it is determined.

$$K_A = C_{3A} - R_3 = 7 - 1 = 6$$
$$R_4 = C_{4A} - K_A = 7 - 6 = 1$$
$$R_8 = C_{8A} - K_A = 0 - 6 = -6$$
$$K_C = C_{3C} - R_3 = 4 - 1 = 3$$
$$R_2 = C_{2C} - K_C = 5 - 3 = 2$$
$$K_M = C_{2M} - R_2 = 3 - 2 = 1$$

Two important points about these computations should be noted. First, the sequence in which the coefficients are determined is, with minor exceptions, significant. Second, there is only one way in which each coefficient can be computed.

Step 3 of the MODI Method uses the row and column coefficients together with the entries in unused cells as shown in Table 5.9. Used cells are not relevant to this step and are omitted from the table.

TABLE 5.9
Determination of Unused Cell Evaluations:
MODI Method

R_i ↓	1	6	3	3	←K_j
0	5	6		6	
	4	0		3	
2		6	6		
		-2	1		
1	5				
	3				
1	6		5	3	
	4		1	-1	
-6	0		0	0	
	5		3	3	

The evaluation of each unused cell proceeds using Equation 5.6,

$$E_{ij} = C_{ij} - (R_i + K_j), \tag{5.6}$$

where

E_{ij} = evaluation or value of unused cell ij,
C_{ij} = cost or profit entry in cell ij,
R_i = row coefficient for ith row, and
K_j = column coefficient for the jth column.

The computations are straightforward:

$$E_{2A} = C_{2A} - (R_2 + K_A) = 6 - (\ 2 + 6) = -2$$
$$E_{1M} = C_{1M} - (R_1 + K_M) = 5 - (\ 0 + 1) = \quad 4$$
$$E_{SM} = C_{SM} - (R_S + K_M) = 0 - (-6 + 1) = \quad 5.$$

Note that these cell evaluations are exactly the same as those obtained by the Stepping-Stone method (see Table 5.7). The beginner may find it helpful to use one as a check on the other. Later, a choice between them can be made on the basis of personal preference.

CHECKING YOUR COMPREHENSION

(Answers will be found at the end of the book)

Check your understanding of the MODI method presented in Section 5.5.2 by answering the questions which follow. Answers are on p. 148.

Questions 12 to 14: The Uni-Product Company

12. Develop an initial solution using the North-to-South Row

Rule (as in Question 4). Assign a zero MODI coefficient to Row 1. Employing *used cells* only, develop the MODI coefficients for all other rows and columns.

13. Use your row and column coefficients to evaluate all *unused* cells.

14. Compare your unused-cell evaluations with those you obtained using the Stepping-Stone method in Questions 10 and 11. They should be exactly the same.

5.6 DEVELOP REVISED MATRIX (*STEP* 5)

As in the simplex method, there are several criteria that may be used to determine which variable (unused cell) should be brought into the solution at any given stage. A logical criterion for the beginning student is the net effect per unit. In our sample problem, this would lead to the conclusion that cell 2–A is the best alternative since it has the highest potential saving.[13]

The —$2 evaluation of unused cell 2–A indicates that the transfer of one unit into this cell, together with compensating adjustments along the evaluation route, will reduce the total cost of the assignment mix by $2. Since the costs within each cell are linear, it would presumably pay to transfer as many units among these cells as is technically feasible. Consequently our interest should now be directed toward determining the maximum number of loads that it is possible to transfer along this route.

---

[13] A total effect criterion (cell value × number of units moved) might also be used. Since the need for reducing computation work is not so great in the transportation as in the simplex method, it makes little difference which criterion is used in elementary problems.

The status of each cell in the initial matrix (Table 5.7) was as follows:

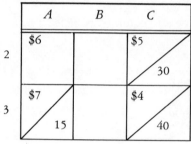

(Cost = $5 × 30 + $7 × 15 + $4 × 40 = $415)

The evaluation for cell 2–A was initiated by tentatively assuming the addition of one unit to that cell. The technical adjustments required to make this change feasible included the addition of one unit to cell 3–C as well as the subtraction of one unit each from cells 2–C and 3–A. The status of these four cells following the transfer of one unit along the evaluation route would be as follows:

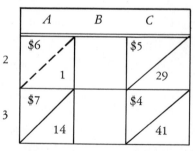

(Cost = $6 × 1 + $5 × 29 + $7 × 14 + $4 × 41 = $413)

Note that the cost of these assignments is $2 less than those of the initial solution. The value of cell 2–A has been saved by the transfer of one unit among these four cells.

If this transfer process were continued, the number of loads within cells 2–A and 3–C would increase while the loads assigned to cells 2–C and 3–A would decrease. Consequently, 15 loads represent the maximum number of units that can be moved along the evaluation route for cell 2–A.

The net decrease in hauling cost represented by this change in the assignment mix would be $30 (15 units at a saving of $2 each). This saving is also demonstrated by the difference between the initial cost of these cell assignments ($415) and the cost of the new or revised assignments derived below ($385):

	A	B	C
2	$6 /15		$5 /15
3	$7		$4 /55

(Cost = $6 × 15 + $5 × 15 + $4 × 55 = $385)

Two general rules may now be stated:

a) If it is desirable to transfer one unit along a favorable evaluation route, the maximum possible number of units should be moved.

b) Since only positive values are allowed for variables, this maximum is determined by that cell within the route having the *smallest* assignment among those cells from which units are to be *subtracted*. In the foregoing example, units were to be transferred from both cell 3–A and cell 2–C. The 15 loads within cell 3–A are the smaller assignment, and this becomes the limiting number for this transfer. Implementation of this change results in a revised matrix (Table 5.10) which represents the second-stage solution.

TABLE 5.10

Second-Stage Solution

		Sources of Hauling Capacity			
		Firm			Material Requirements
Site	M	A	B	C	
No. 1	$5	$6	$3 / 60	$6	60
No. 2	$3 / 60	$6 / 15	$6	$5 / 15	90
No. 3	$5	$7	$4 / 20	$4 / 55	75
No. 4	$6	$7 / 65	$5	$3	65
Slack	$0	$0 / 20	$0	$0	20
Hauling Capacity	60	100	80	70	310

CHECKING YOUR COMPREHENSION

(Answers will be found at the end of the book)

Check your ability to develop a revised matrix (Section 5.6) by performing the operations indicated below. Answers are given on p. 149.

Questions *15 to 17:* The Uni-Product Company

15. Use your evaluations of unused cells from questions 11 and/

or 13 to identify that cell which should be brought into solution.

16. What is the evaluation route for this cell? How many units (carloads) can be moved along this route?

17. Develop the matrix which describes the second-stage solution for this problem.

5.7 REPEAT STEPS 3–5 UNTIL AN OPTIMUM SOLUTION IS PROVED BY STEP 4 (*STEP* 6)

The cost of the second-stage solution is $1,280, $30 less than that of the initial solution. Is it the best possible or optimum solution? Only when *Step 4* shows no unused cells with favorable evaluations can we prove that the search for improved solutions may be terminated. *Step 6* simply reminds us that linear programming is an iterative process.

5.7.1 *Steps 3 to 5* (Second Stage)

All unused cells must be evaluated after each transfer of units has been made, since the evaluation routes for many cells will be changed as a result. Table 5.10 represents the second-stage solution and should be subjected to *Steps 3, 4,* and *5*. Note that cell 2–A is now a used cell. Also, cell 3–A has become an unused cell and is therefore no longer eligible as part of (a) an evaluation route, or (b) the MODI coefficient determination.

The solution is first subjected to the Rim − 1 test for degeneracy. Then the evaluation of unused cells proceeds using either of the methods demonstrated previously. The MODI coefficients and cell evaluations corresponding to the second-stage solution are shown in Table 5.11.

Examination of the matrix discloses that several evaluation routes and cell evaluations have indeed changed from those appropriate to the initial solution of Table 5.7. The effects on cell

4–C illustrate this point. The route for this cell in Table 5.7 was
4–C, 4–A, 3–A, 3–C. The initial analysis resulted in the with-
drawal of all units from cell 3–A, making it an unused cell. At
the same time, cell 2–A was changed from an unused to a used
cell so that it is now eligible for evaluation routes. The revised
route for cell 4–C in Table 5.11 is now 4–C, 4–A, 2–A, 2–C.
The new evaluation is −$3 per load as contrasted to the $1 saving (−$1 value) found in the initial solution.

Table 5.11 also indicates that cells 4–B and 4–C have negative

TABLE 5.11

Cell Evaluations: Second-Stage Solution

Sources of Hauling Capacity					
			Firm		
		M	A	B	C	
Site		1	4	3	3	*Material Requirements*
No. 1	0	$5 +4	$6 +2	$3 / 60	$6 +3	60
No. 2	2	$3 / 60	$6 / 15	$6 +1	$5 / 15	90
No. 3	1	$5 +3	$7 +2	$4 / 20	$4 / 55	75
No. 4	3	$6 +2	$7 / 65	$5 (−1)	$3* (−3)	65
Slack	−4	$0 +3	$0 / 20	$0 +1	$0 +1	20
Hauling Capacity		60	100	80	70	310

values—they represent opportunities to reduce cost. Based upon the net-effect-per-unit criterion, cell 4–C should be selected for introduction into the solution. The transfer of units into cell 4–C (and cell 2–A as well) will require that a corresponding number of loads be transferred from cells 4–A and 2–C. The units within cell 2–C (15) represent the limiting factor in determining the maximum number of units to be exchanged. The expected cost saving that would result from this change would be $45 (15 × $3). Implementation of these changes in assignments produces the third stage, as shown in Table 5.12.

TABLE 5.12

Third-Stage Solution

Sources of Hauling Capacity

		Firm				
		M	A	B	C	*Material*
Site		4	7	3	3	*Requirements*
No. 1	0	$5 / 1	$6 / (−1)	$3 / 60	$6 / 3	60
No. 2	−1	$3 / 60	$6 / 30	$6 / 4	$5 / 3	90
No. 3	1	$5 / 0	$7 / (−1)	$4 / 20	$4 / 55	75
No. 4	0	$6 / 2	$7 / 50	$5 / 2	$3 / 15	65
Slack	−7	$0 / 3	$0 / 20	$0 / 4	$0 / 4	20
Hauling Capacity		60	100	80	70	310

5.7.2 Steps 3 to 5 (Third Stage)

Examination of Table 5.12 shows that two cells (1–A and 3–A) now have identical negative values. Since the evaluation path of 3–A is the simpler one, suppose that it is selected. Fifty units would be shifted between cells 3–A, 3–C, 4–C, and 4–A. The fourth-stage solution that results (Table 5.13) is shown to be optimal in that there are no cells having a favorable (negative) evaluation.[14]

The total cost of this solution is as follows.

Site No. 1: $3 × 60	= $	180
Site No. 2: $3 × 60 + $6 × 30	=	360
Site No. 3: $7 × 50 + $4 × 20 + $4 × 5 =		450
Site No. 4: $3 × 65	=	195
		$1,185

It is interesting to note that this optimal set of assignments represents a $125 saving over the cost of the initial solution. This reduction was achieved by changing the assignments for Sites No. 2, No. 3, and No. 4. The cost of hauling materials to Sites No. 2 and No. 3 was actually increased in the process by $30 and $105 respectively, but this increase was compensated for by a large decrease ($260) in the cost for Site No. 4. The criterion adopted was that of minimizing total cost for the system as a whole since it is impossible to minimize hauling cost to each individual site. Use of the transportation method of linear programming in the analysis of the allocation decision made the accomplishment of this objective possible.

---

[14] In a cost minimization problem such as our example, a "favorable" cell evaluation would be negative, that is, an opportunity to decrease cost. When the objective function represents a form of profit maximization, positive cell evaluations would be considered "favorable."

TABLE 5.13
Fourth-Stage (Optimal) Solution

Site		Firm M	A	B	C	Material Requirements
		3	6	3	3	
No. 1	0	$5 / +2	$6 / 0	$3 / 60	$6 / +3	60
No. 2	0	$3 / 60	$6 / 30	$6 / +3	$5 / +2	90
No. 3	1	$5 / +1	$7 / 50	$4 / 20	$4 / 5	75
No. 4	0	$6 / +3	$7 / +1	$5 / +2	$3 / 65	65
Slack	−6	$0 / +3	$0 / 20	$0 / +3	$0 / +3	20
Hauling Capacity		60	100	80	70	310

Sources of Hauling Capacity (column heading above Firm)

CHECKING YOUR COMPREHENSION
(Answers will be found at the end of the book)

Test your ability to carry a transportation problem to an optimal solution as described in Section 5.7 by performing the operations outlined below. The answers are provided on p. 149.

Questions *18 to 22:* The Uni-Product Company

18. Evaluate the following unused cells in your second-stage

matrix developed for question 17. Identify each route.

a) B–3   *c*) D–4   *e*) Slack — 3
b) C–2   *d*) A–4   *f*) Slack — 4

19. Evaluate all other unused cells.

20. Select the cell which should now be introduced. Determine the number of units which should be moved along its evaluation route.

21. Develop the third-stage matrix.

22. Evaluate all unused cells in the third stage. (This is the optimal solution). Indicate how you can identify this as the optimal solution.

5.8 INTERPRETATION FOR IMPLEMENTATION

The interpretation of assignments within an optimal transportation matrix is relatively straightforward. For example, Table 5.13 indicates that the McClain fleet should be assigned to Site No. 2, that only 80 of the 100 loads offered by Firm A should be accepted, and so forth. What additional information might be important to the decision-maker?

One item of possible interest results from the zero-cell evaluation in cell 1–A as presented in Table 5.13. This shows that there is a *range* of optimal solutions, that is, units can be moved into cell 1–A without changing the cost of the optimal solution. For example, we could move 50 units around the evaluation route for this cell (1–A, 1–B, 3–B, 3–A) and still minimize total hauling cost. For reasons outside the linear programming analysis (quality of service possibly), the decision-maker might prefer this alternative optimal solution.

The evaluations for other unused cells could also be of interest since they represent the opportunity cost of utilizing these assignments. For example, the decision-maker might ask what the consequences would be of assigning the slack to Firm B rather than Firm A. The +3 evalution in cell S–B means that total cost would be increased by $3 for each load moved into this cell. Whether the gains in other relevant but non-quantitative factors in the decision would justify this increase in cost would have to be resolved by the judgment of the decision-maker.

5.9 METHOD FOR HANDLING DEGENERATE SOLUTIONS

The initial solution developed using the Northwest Corner Rule (Table 5.4) proved to be degenerate; the number of used cells was less than Rim − 1. For this reason, the discussion of *Steps 4* and *5* was limited to optimizing the North to South Row inspection solution. Now that the reader is familiar with the basic computational procedure, the methods for handling degenerate solutions will be demonstrated.

Degeneracy can appear in an initial or any subsequent solution. To restore the number of used cells to Rim − 1, assign some very small number of units ϵ (epsilon) to one of the unused cells. By definition this number is so small that it has no effect when added to or subtracted from any positive integer. For example, $90 + \epsilon = 90$ and $10 - \epsilon = 10$.

The particular unused cell selected for ϵ units is important. In Table 5.14, for example, it is not possible to compute the row and column MODI coefficients unless the ϵ is placed in either Row 1 or Column M.[15] Normally, the cell having the lowest cost (or highest profit) would be selected (1–B in this case). However, for purposes of illustration, we select cell 1–A and proceed to determine MODI coefficients as shown in Table 5.15.

---

[15] The ease with which the MODI method signals degeneracy as well as indicates the cell alternatives for ϵ is an advantage.

TABLE 5.14

Initial Solution: Northwest Corner Rule
Alternative Adjustments for Degeneracy

R_i $\downarrow$	$K_M = 5$	$K_A =$	$K_B =$	$K_C =$	$\leftarrow K_j$
$R_1 = 0$	5 / 60				
$R_2 =$		6 / 90			
$R_3 =$		7 / 10	4 / 65		
$R_4 =$			5 / 15	3 / 50	
$R_S =$				0 / 20	

The ϵ cell appears (Table 5.15) in the evaluation route of cell 1–B and is the limiting cell for movement of units. In accordance with the previous definition, we ignore the addition to and subtraction of ϵ from all cells except 1–A and 1–B. The former becomes an unused cell (since $\epsilon - \epsilon = 0$), while the latter becomes the ϵ cell $(0 + \epsilon = \epsilon)$ as in Table 5.16. Thus the only change in this second-stage solution is to move the assignment of epsilon from cell 1–A to 1–B.[16]

Inspection of the cell evaluations in Table 5.16 indicates that $7 per load can be saved by transferring five units over the

---

[16] This illustrates the fact that cell 1–B should have been selected for ϵ in the first place. More important, this shows how changes are made when units are to be transferred from the ϵ cell.

TABLE 5.15

Initial Solution Modified for Degeneracy

Sources of Hauling Capacity

Site		Firm				Material Requirements
		M	A	B	C	
		5	6	8	6	
No. 1	0	$5 / 60	$6 / ε	$3 / −5	$6 / 0	60
No. 2	0	$3 / −2	$6 / 90	$6 / −2	$5 / −1	90
No. 3	−4	$5 / −4	$7 / 5	$4 / 75	$4 / 2	75
No. 4	−3	$6 / −4	$7 / −4	$5 / 5	$3 / 60	65
Slack	−6	$0 / 1	$0 / 10	$0 / −2	$0 / 10	20
Hauling Capacity		60	100	80	70	310

route 2–M, 1–M, 1–B, 4–B, 4–C, S–C, S–A, 2–A. While the ε cell (1–B) appears in this route, it presents no problems since units are to be added to it and, by definition, $5 + \epsilon = 5$.

Note that the solution which results from these changes (Table 5.17) has eight used cells with legitimate assignments. Degeneracy can "disappear" as well as appear in this sense at any stage.

5.10 SUMMARY

The transportation like the graphical method is a special

TABLE 5.16

Second-Stage Solution: Degeneracy Illustration

Sources of Hauling Capacity

Site		Firm M 5	A 1	B 3	C 1	*Material Requirements*
No. 1	0	$5 / 60	$6 / 5	$3 / ε	$6 / 5	60
No. 2	5	$3 / (−7)	$6 / 90	$6 / −2	$5 / −1	90
No. 3	1	$5 / −1	$7 / 5	$4 / 75	$4 / 2	75
No. 4	2	$6 / −1	$7 / 4	$5 / 5	$3 / 60	65
Slack	−1	$0 / −4	$0 / 10	$0 / −2	$0 / 10	20
Hauling Capacity		60	100	80	70	310

case of the more general simplex method. The key characteristic which permits the simplified format of this method is homogeneity. This means that the rate of substitution between all variables relative to all restrictions is one to one.

The computation procedure centers on a matrix that displays all variables in the problem (cells) and the restrictions (rim requirements) for both sources and destinations.

The analysis starts with the development of an initial solution. This may be done using the Northwest Corner Rule or some inspection method such as the North to South Row Rule.

TABLE 5.17
Third-Stage Solution: Degeneracy Illustration

Sources of Hauling Capacity

Site		M	A	B	C	Material Requirements
		Firm				
		5	8	3	8	
No. 1	0	$5 / 55	$6 −2	$3 / 5	$6 −2	60
No. 2	−2	$3 / 5	$6 / 85	$6 5	$5 −1	90
No. 3	1	$5 −1	$7 −2	$4 / 75	$4 5	75
No. 5	−5	$6 6	$7 4	$5 7	$3 / 65	65
Slack	−8	$0 3	$0 / 15	$0 5	$0 / 5	20
Hauling Capacity		60	100	80	70	310

Degeneracy can occur in any linear programming problem but it is especially frequent in the transportation method. The Rim − 1 is a test for degeneracy which must be applied to all solutions. When degeneracy is indicated, an artificial used cell with a very small (ϵ) assignment is created so that the computation procedure may be continued.

Unused cells may be evaluated by using either the Stepping-Stone or the MODI Method. Those cells having a favorable effect on the objective function are brought into the solution by assigning the maximum possible number of units to them. Each new matrix created in this manner is evaluated until an optimal solution is indicated by the evaluation process for unused cells.

5.11 REVIEW QUESTIONS

1. Explain where the following characteristics are reflected in the McClain Co. and Uni-Product problems: (a) Linearity; (b) certainty; (c) homogeneity.

2. Why is slack frequently needed in transportation problems? Under what special circumstances would slack *not* be needed?

3. What criterion must the initial solution to a transportation format problem meet? Would the availability of a computer influence your choice of an initial solution method?

4. Explain briefly the procedure for evaluating unused cells using the Stepping-Stone method. Under what circumstances would "plus" cell evaluations be considered favorable?

5. Why do some of the following change from one stage to another?
   a) Evaluation routes;
   b) MODI coefficients;
   c) evaluations of unused cells.

6. Indicate how you could recognize a degenerate solution when using the following:
   a) Rim — Rule;
   b) Stepping-Stone method;
   c) MODI coefficients.

7. What condition indicates that an optimal solution has been reached in the transportation method?

8. Use your knowledge of the more general simplex method to explain the logic of the following rules in the transportation method:
   a) Only used cells may be utilized in establishing evaluation routes for unused cells.
   b) Each new used cell must displace a former used cell.

5.12 EXERCISES

1. The matrix which follows gives the costs associated with allocating a set of "sources" to three alternative "destinations" and an initial solution.

Destinations

	D_1	D_2	D_3	
S_1	$4 / 20	$7 / 80	$3	100
S_2	$2	$4	$5 / 50	50
S_3	$8 / 20	$6	$1 / 50	70
	40	80	100	

Sources

a) What is the total cost of this solution? (*Ans.:* $1,100)

b) Evaluate all unused cells using the Stepping-Stone method. (*Ans.:* $S_1D_3 = +6; S_2D_1 = -10; S_2D_2 = -11; S_3D_2 = -5$)

c) Compute MODI coefficients and evaluate unused cells. (*Ans.:* $R = 0, 8, 4; K = 4, 7, -3$)

d) What cell should be selected for implementation and how many units will be transferred? (*Ans.:* 20 units in S_2D_2; route is $S_1D_2, S_1D_1, S_3D_1, S_3D_3, S_2D_3$)

e) Construct the second-stage matrix. Compute MODI and evaluate unused cells. Select a cell for implementation. (*Ans.:* $R = 0, -3, -7; K = 4, 7, 8. S_1D_3 = -5$. Move 30 units over route S_1D_2, S_2D_2, S_2D_3)

f) Construct the third-stage matrix. Show that it is the optimal solution. Compute the total cost. (*Ans.:* $730)

2. The Beeman Company manufactures a specialized replacement part for the automotive trade. Sold at a fixed delivered price per unit of $2.95, the part is distributed through five independent wholesalers on the west coast. Two weeks ago the Beeman sales department issued the official sales forecast for the next quarter.

Forecasted Monthly Deliveries in Units to Wholesalers

Wholesaler	Deliveries
A	3,000
B	3,000
C	10,000
D	5,000
E	4,000
Total	25,000

Production is carried out in three manufacturing plants which are expected to have the following cost and capacity characteristics during the next quarter:

Plant Characteristics

Plant Number	Monthly Production Capacity	Production Costs Fixed (Overhead) (per month)	Variable (per unit)
1	5,000 units	$ 6,000	$1.10
2	10,000 units	10,000	1.00
3	12,500 units	12,000	0.90

Since Beeman absorbs freight charges on all outgoing shipments, the company has traditionally been very careful to watch transportation costs. Rates for the next several months between plants and wholesalers are as follows:

Freight Costs
(dollars per unit)

From Plant Number	To Wholesaler				
	A	B	C	D	E
1	0.06	0.08	0.11	0.16	0.16
2	0.09	0.07	0.10	0.13	0.15
3	0.11	0.10	0.09	0.11	0.16

Last week the V.P. of Manufacturing, using the company's "customary policy" for allocating forecasted demand to manufacturing facilities, established the following planned production levels for the various plants:

Plant No. 1— 3,000 units per month
Plant No. 2— 9,500 units per month
Plant No. 3—12,500 units per month

The manager of Plant No. 1 has appealed this decision since he feels it will not only raise his cost per unit, but also that it is an uneconomical allocation for the company as a whole. Excerpts from his appeal letter follow:

The proposed allocation means my plant will be operating at only 60% of capacity. As a consequence our full cost per unit will be over three dollars as shown by the following computation:

$$\frac{\$6,000 + \$1.10\ (3,000)}{\$3,000} = \$3.10 \text{ per unit.}$$

At the same time, Bill, over in Plant 3, will be operating at 100% and get all the advantages of spreading his fixed costs over a large volume, so his cost per unit will be very favorable:

$$\frac{\$12,000 + \$0.90\ (12,500)}{12,500} = \$1.86 \text{ per unit.}$$

As an alternative, I propose that you switch at least 2,000 units from his plant to ours. The added volume will reduce our cost per unit far more than it will increase his. For example:

$$\frac{\$6,000 + \$1.10\ (5,000)}{5,000} = \$2.30 \text{ per unit in No. 1,}$$

$$\frac{\$12,000 + \$0.90\ (10,500)}{10,500} = \$2.04 \text{ per unit in No. 3.}$$

Thus we will save 80¢ on cost here in No. 1 while Plant 3's will increase only 18¢ per unit. That means a net saving of 62¢ on 2,000 units or a total reduction in cost of goods sold of $1,240 each month during the next quarter. Since we are currently on a profit improvement program, I urge that you consider and adopt this proposed change in our production plan.

a) Construct a matrix for solution of the problem using freight cost from plants to warehouses only. Develop an initial solution using a West to East Row Rule, that is, minimize the freight cost in column A, then B, and so forth. What implications does this solution have for the company's "customary policy" on allocation of demand to plants?

b) Carry your matrix from (a) to an optimal solution. Determine total freight cost per month.

c) Construct a second matrix. This time include the sum of two components in the cost of each cell: (1) variable cost of production per unit, and (2) freight cost per unit. For example, the cost of cell 1–A would include the cost to manufacture in Plant 1 plus the freight cost to Wholesaler A.

d) Perform the iterations necessary to optimize the matrix.

e) Does your analysis suggest any possible changes in the company's "customary" allocation policy? Explain.

f) Prepare a short reply to the letter from the Plant 1 manager.

3. The numbers within the cells of the matrix in the accompanying table represent the expected cost per unit of assigning a series of shop orders (1–4) to each of four work stations (A–D). The number of units required per order and the available capacities of each work station are also shown. The total production cost for the series of orders is to be minimized.

a) Develop an initial solution using the North to South Row Rule.

b) Determine the cost of your initial solution.

c) Carry the problem to an optimal solution using as many matrices as necessary.

d) Determine the total cost of your optimal solution.

e) Assuming that maximizing R.O.I. is the highest-order economic objective of this firm, justify the use of total cost as the measure of effectiveness in this problem.

	Work Stations				
Order	A	B	C	D	Requirements
No. 1	8¢	5¢	4¢	6¢	65
No. 2	10¢	7¢	5¢	3¢	60
No. 3	6¢	5¢	7¢	4¢	55
No. 4	8¢	9¢	6¢	5¢	30
Capacity	25	65	45	75	210

f) Where is homogeneity a characteristic in this problem? What problems might you encounter in framing this problem from raw machine and order data?

g) Under what circumstances would slack be necessary in a problem of this general type? What would slack represent in each case?

4. Use the Northwest Corner Rule to develop an initial solution to Problem 3.

a) Will the optimal solution be the same as in Problem 3?

b) What difference (compared to Problem 3) would you expect in carrying this solution to the optimum?

c) Illustrate your claims in Problem 4*b* by carrying your initial solution to the optimum.

5. Hoolihan Stores, Inc., a chain organization with four retail stores, is negotiating with four potential suppliers for next month's supply of an item. The maximum number of crates offered by each vendor is as follows: *A*—400; *B*—650; *C*—450; and *D*—800.

The buyer for this item has made a careful analysis of vendor prices, transportation charges, store operating costs, and other cost factors. His analysis shows the following expected profit margin per crate:

	Vendor			
Store	*A*	*B*	*C*	*D*
1......$0.90		$0.60	$0.50	$0.70
2...... 1.10		0.80	0.60	0.60
3...... —		0.60	0.80	0.50
4...... 0.80		1.00	0.70	0.60

The merchandise carried by Vendor *A* is not suitable for Store 3; therefore Vendor *A* was not asked to bid on this requirement.

a) The expected requirements (in crates) at each store during June are: 1—750; 2—600; 3—550; and 4—300.

1. Construct the matrix for this problem.

2. Develop an initial solution.

3. Carry the problem to an optimal solution and explain the meaning of your final matrix.

b) July's requirements at each store are expected to increase over the June level by 50 units.

1. Assuming vendor capacities and expected profit margins remain the same, develop the decision matrix for the July buying decision.
2. Develop an optimal solution and explain its meaning.

6. The Reitzson Company operates four manufacturing plants. Shipments are made to four warehouses which fill customer orders from stock. Plant 1 is the company's original manufacturing facility. The family which owns the controlling interest in the firm still resides in the community. Plants 2 and 3 were constructed during the post-war period. Plant 4 is in the first few months of full-scale operation.

a) Each warehouse prepares a sales forecast for each planning period and forwards it to company headquarters at Plant 1. The company president has always prided himself on securing the lowest possible freight charges. As a consequence, all production scheduling has been based upon minimizing total transportation costs for goods shipped between manufacturing plants and company-owned warehouses.

The freight charges per unit from each plant to each warehouse are as follows:

	Plant			
Warehouse	1	2	3	4
A	$ 9	$ 6	$ 8	$ 7
B	5	8	9	9
C	10	11	9	8
D	7	6	5	8

The expected requirements and maximum plant capacities for the next planning period are as follows:

Warehouse A:	3100 units	Plant 1:	1200 units
B:	1800 units	Plant 2:	4200 units
C:	2000 units	Plant 3:	5000 units
D:	4400 units	Plant 4:	2000 units

1. In order to minimize transportation charges for the period, what production level should be established for each plant?

b) The production manager has never been very happy about the method used to determine master production schedules. He suggests that the results of a recent production cost analysis should be incorporated in the decision:

	Plant			
	1	2	3	4
Standard Cost	$63(?)	$53	$52	$56
Regular Capacity	1200	3600	4200	2000
Overtime Capacity	——	600	800	——
Overtime Cost	——	$64	$62	——

The production manager explains that the so-called standard cost for Plant 1 is actually about $60 up to 900 units. The poor layout and antiquated equipment result in congestion and inefficiencies at all output figures above 900 units. As a consequence, the last 300 units of capacity actually cost $68 each.

1. Develop a scheduling matrix which incorporates both transportation and production cost factors.

2. What output levels should be established for each manufacturing plant during the next planning period?

c) The personnel manager at Plant 1 warns that a strike is imminent. The issues involved are difficult and emotional ones. He suggests that Plant 1 may not be in operation during the next planning period. The president asks that an alternative output schedule be developed based on the assumption that Plant 1 will be closed during the period. The production manager and the Plant 4 manager have an informal agreement that no overtime production will be required this year.

1. Develop the schedule requested by the president.

7. The Smith Manufacturing Company is scheduling the output of its assembly operations for the next three planning periods. The company assembles two products, A and B. The expected requirements are as follows:

Period 1	Period 2	Period 3
225 A units	375 A units	450 A units
200 B units	260 B units	300 B units

Regular assembly capacity is 100 hours per period. The following overtime hours have also been authorized: Period 1—30 hours; Period 2—40 hours; Period 3—30 hours. Each A item requires 0.2 hour and each B item requires 0.25 hour of assembly time. No back ordering is allowed.

Production of both A and B items on overtime results in additional costs of $2.00 per unit. The inventory carrying cost of A items is $1.00 per unit for the first period and $1.20 per unit for the second period following the month of their production. Storage cost for B units is $1.00 per unit for the first period and $1.25 per unit for the second period.

a) Develop the matrix for this problem. (*Hint:* Use capacities as sources and requirements as destinations.)

b) Use the Northwest Corner Rule for the initial solution.

c) Determine the quantities of each product to be manufactured during each period, if total penalty cost over the three periods is to be minimized.

d) Interpret your optimal matrix. What instructions would you give the assembly foreman?

e) If backorders were allowed, how would your matrix differ from the one used above?

Appendix

AN ALTERNATIVE COMPUTATIONAL PROCEDURE FOR REVISION OF SIMPLEX TABLES

Step 4 in the simplex method requires that a revised set of coefficients and production data be computed for each new table. The method suggested for performing this task in Chapter 4 was based on the use of physical rates of substitution among the several resources in a problem. This was a logical method for the beginning student since we were concerned with demonstrating why as well as how the computational procedure works. However, this method is also a tedious one which is somewhat awkward in working large problems by hand. Here we give an alternative method for computing new coefficients and outputs which is both shorter and more efficient.

The procedure begins with the selection of the *Key column.* This is simply the column within the current table for the variable selected for introduction in the next stage. For example, the analysis of Section 4.4 (*Step 3*) indicated that sugar cookies should be introduced into the origin solution. Thus, the *Key column* in Table 4.3 is the *S* column.

Next, one must select the *Key row*. This is the row of coefficients within the current table for the variable which is to be displaced. In the bakery example sugar cookies were to replace *O* cookies in the second stage. Thus the *Key row* in Table 4.3 is the *O* row.

Third, the *Key number* is identified. This is simply the coefficient which falls at the intersection of the Key column and row. The *Key number* in Table 4.3 would be the 1.0 at the intersection of the *S* column and *O* row.

Once the Key column, row, and number have been established, the computation of revised data for the next stage proceeds in two distinct steps.

1. First, the coefficients and production for the replacement row in the next table are computed.

$$\text{Replacement row coefficients} = \frac{\text{old Key row coefficients}}{\text{Key number}};$$
$$(A.1)$$

$$\text{Replacement row production} = \frac{\text{old Key row production}}{\text{Key number}}.$$
$$(A.2)$$

The relevant sections of Table 4.3, or the origin solution for the bakery problem, are reproduced in Table A.1. Recall that sugar cookies (Key column) are to replace *O* cookies (Key row) in the next stage. The Key number at the intersection is 1.0.

TABLE A.1

Origin Solution: Key Row and Column Circled

	I	*S*	*L*	*O*	*M*	*Production*
L	0.15	0.10	1	0	0	15
O	1.0	1.0	0	1	0	120
M	0.4	0.0	0	0	1	32

Equation A.1 would be applied to the Key row of Table A.1 in the following manner:

$$I = \frac{1.0}{1.0} = 1, \quad S = \frac{1.0}{1.0} = 1, \quad L = \frac{0}{1.0} = 0,$$

$$O = \frac{1}{1.0} = 1, \quad M = \frac{0}{1.0} = 0.$$

In like manner Equation A.2 would apply in determining the new production figure for the replacement row $(S$ replaces $O)$:

$$\text{Production of } S = \frac{120}{1.0} = 120.$$

These data can now be transferred to the appropriate row in the table for the next stage (see Table 4.5).[1]

2. Revised coefficients and production data for all additional rows in the new matrix may now be computed using the following equations:

New coefficient =

$$\text{old coefficient} - \left(\begin{array}{c} \text{corresponding} \\ \text{coefficient of} \\ \text{Key row} \end{array} \right) \left(\dfrac{\begin{array}{c}\text{corresponding} \\ \text{coefficient of} \\ \text{Key column} \end{array}}{\text{Key number}} \right);$$

$$(\text{A.3})$$

New production =

$$\text{old production} - \left(\begin{array}{c} \text{corresponding} \\ \text{production of} \\ \text{Key row} \end{array} \right) \left(\dfrac{\begin{array}{c}\text{corresponding} \\ \text{coefficient of} \\ \text{Key column} \end{array}}{\text{Key number}} \right).$$

$$(\text{A.4})$$

---

[1] The fact that the Key number was 1.0 in this illustration represents a special case. When the Key number does not equal one, the revised coefficients will be different from those in the Key row, as will be shown in a subsequent example.

Equations A.3 and A.4 would be applied to the first (L) row of Table A.1 in the following manner:

$$\text{New } I = 0.15 - 1.0 \left(\frac{.10}{1.0} \right) = \ \ 0.15 - 1.0 \left(0.10 \right) = 0.05;$$

$$\text{new } S = 0.10 - 1.0 \left(\frac{.10}{1.0} \right) = \ \ 0.10 - 1.0 \left(0.10 \right) = 0;$$

$$\text{new } L = 1 \ \ -0 \ \ (0.10) = \ \ 1;$$

$$\text{new } O = 0 \ \ -1 \ \ (0.10) = -0.10; \text{ and}$$

$$\text{new } M = 0 \ \ -0 \ \ (0.10) = \ \ 0.$$

The new production number for the L row can be computed using Equation A.4:

$$\text{New production } (L) = 15 - 120 \ \frac{.10}{1.0} = 3.$$

Computation of the new coefficients for the M row of Table A.1 would proceed as follows:

$$\text{New } L = 0.4 - 1.0 \left(\frac{0.0}{1.0} \right) = 0.4 - 0 = 0.4,$$

$$\text{New } S = 0.0 - 1.0 \left(\frac{0.0}{1.0} \right) = 0.$$

At this point one should recognize the fact that the coefficients and production will remain *unchanged* from the previous stage for all rows in the Key column which contain a *zero* coefficient. The reason for this is evident in the two calculations shown above. The 0.0 in the Key (S) column for the M row makes the second term in Equations A.3 and A.4 equal to zero, so that the "old" coefficients remain unchanged from one stage to the next.[2] Knowing this, we can now simply copy the M coefficients directly

---

[2] We can generalize still further and state that no changes in row data will take place if either of the two corresponding coefficients in the second term are equal to zero.

from Table A.1 to Table A.2 which represents the second-stage solution.

TABLE A.2

Second-Stage Solution: Key Row and Column Circled

	I	S	L	O	M	*Production*
L	0.05	0	1	−0.10	0	3
S	1	1	0	1	0	120
M	0.4	0	0	0	1	32

One additional illustration showing how these equations may be used to compute the new matrix may be helpful. Consider the second-stage solution of Table A.2. The analysis to determine which variable to introduce in the next stage proceeds as outlined in Section 4.4. This analysis indicated that iced cookies were to be introduced (Key column) and that the L variable was to be displaced (Key row). The Key number is therefore 0.05.

First, we apply Equation A.1 to determine the coefficients for I in the replacement row:

$$I = \frac{0.05}{0.05} = 1, \quad S = \frac{0}{0.05} = 0, \quad L = \frac{1}{0.05} = 20,$$

$$O = \frac{-0.10}{0.05} = -2, \quad M = \frac{0}{0.05} = 0.$$

The production figure for I is

$$Q_I = \frac{3}{0.05} = 60.$$

These data can now be entered in the new first row of Table A.3 which represents the third-stage solution.

Next, we use Equations A.3 and A.4 to compute new numbers for all other rows in the matrix:

	Row S	Row M

I $1 - 0.05 \left(\dfrac{1}{0.05} \right) =$ $\qquad$ $0.4 - 0.05 \left(\dfrac{0.4}{0.05} \right) =$
$1 - 0.05\,(20) = 0$ $\qquad$ $0.4 - 0.05\,(8) = 0$

S $1 - 0 \left(\dfrac{1}{0.05} \right) =$ $\qquad$ $0 - 0 \left(\dfrac{0.4}{0.05} \right) =$
$1 - 0\,(20) = 1$ $\qquad$ $0 - 0\,(8) = 0$

L $0 - 1\,(20) = -20$ $\qquad$ $0 - 1\,(8) = -8$

O $1 - (-0.10)(20) = 3$ $\qquad$ $0 - (-0.10)(8) = 0.8$

M $0 - 0\,(20) = 0$ $\qquad$ $1 - 0\,(8) = 1$

Production $120 - 3\,(20) = 60$ $\qquad$ $32 - 3\,(8) = 8.$

These data complete the remaining rows for Table A.3. The corresponding table in the text is 4.6, the complete table for the third-stage solution.

TABLE A.3
Third-Stage Solution

	I	S	L	O	M	Production
I	1	0	20	−2	0	60
S	0	1	−20	3	0	60
M	0	0	−8	0.8	1	8

Answers for Checking Your Comprehension

Answers 1 to 4: The Zeus Company (A)

1. Each standard unit produced next month will require 2 hours and each deluxe unit 3 hours of machining capacity. The sum of these two requirements must be equal to or less than the total capacity of 24,000 hours available.

2. $3 Q_D + 2 Q_S \leq 24,000$.

3. See Figure 3.7.

4. $Q_D = 8,000 - \frac{2}{3} Q_S$.

   Intercepts: deluxe $= 8,000$; standard $= 12,000$.

   Exchange rate: 2 to 3. Two deluxe units can be added to the mix only if 3 standard units are withdrawn (and vice versa).

   TROUBLE? Reread Section 3.1.1 (p. 21).

   ANSWERS OK? Proceed to Questions 5 to 8 (p. 29).

FIGURE 3.7

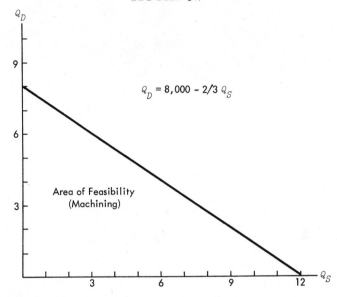

$Q_D = 8,000 - 2/3\ Q_S$

Area of Feasibility
(Machining)

Answers 5 to 8: The Zeus Company (A)

5. $3\ Q_D + 4\ Q_S \leq 36,000$
    $1\ Q_D + \qquad \leq 6,000.$

6. $Q_D = 12,000 - \dfrac{4}{3}\ Q_S.$

    Intercepts: deluxe = 12,000; standard = 9,000.
    Exchange rate: 4 deluxe to 3 standard.
    $Q_D = 6,000.$
    Intercepts: deluxe = 6,000; standard = none.
    Exchange rate: Does not apply since standard model re-
    quires no painting.

7. See Figure 3.8.
    Feasible mixes must plot within or on the rim of the polygon.
    Examples: $(Q_S = 2,000,\ Q_D = 3,000)$; $(9,000, 0)$;
    $(6,000, 4,000)$; $(3,000, 6,000)$.
    Nonfeasible combinations plot outside the polygon.
    Examples: $(2,000, 8,000)$; $(9,000, 1,000)$; $(6,000,$
    $6,000)$; $(3,000, 7,000)$.

FIGURE 3.8

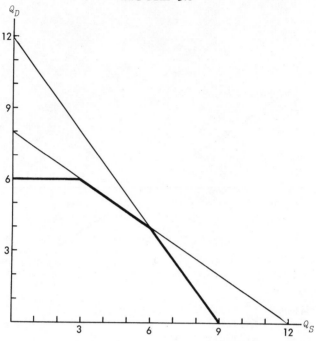

8. Bottleneck for standard will likely be warehouse space. Most severe restriction for deluxe model is painting.

   TROUBLE? Reread Section 3.1.2 (p. 24).

   ANSWERS OK? Proceed to Section 3.2 (p. 30).

Anwers 9 and *10:* The Zeus Company (B)

9. $\$3\,Q_D + \$1\,Q_S = \text{T.C.}$

10. The objective is to find that unique set of values for Q_D and Q_S which fall within the restriction equations and maximize the value of the objective function.

    TROUBLE? Reread Section 3.2 (p. 30).

    ANSWERS OK? Read Section 3.3 (p. 33).

Answers *11* to *14:* The Zeus Company

11. Your plot should show a set of parallel lines with slope of

1 to 3 (if deluxe units on vertical axis). The optimal solution occurs at 3,000 standard and 6,000 deluxe units. The value of the objective function at this point is $21,000.

12. Optimal solutions always lie on the perimeter because we are trying to "move as far away from the origin as possible," that is, to maximize the objective function. In the special case where the slope of the objective function is parallel to one of the critical constraints, there will be a range of optimal solutions. Otherwise, "as far away as possible" means one of the points on the polygon.

13. Solving equations for vertices:

Machine and Warehouse	*Machine and Paint*

$$8,000 - \frac{2}{3} S = 12,000 - \frac{4}{3} S \qquad\qquad 8,000 - \frac{2}{3} S = 6,000$$

$$S = 6,000 \qquad\qquad\qquad\qquad S = 3,000$$

$$D = 8,000 - \frac{2}{3} (6,000) \qquad\qquad D = 8,000 - \frac{2}{3} (3,000)$$

$$= 4,000. \qquad\qquad\qquad\qquad = 6,000.$$

The intersection of warehouse and paint restrictions is not relevant since this occurs outside the polygon.

14. Evaluation of basic solutions:

Points	S	D	Objective Function
B	0	6,000	$18,000
C	3,000	6,000	$21,000 (optimal)
D	6,000	4,000	$18,000
E	9,000	0	$ 9,000

TROUBLE? Reread Section 3.3 (p. 33).

ANSWERS OK? Proceed to Section 3.4 (p. 34).

CHAPTER 4—THE SIMPLEX METHOD

Answers 1 to 4: The Zeus Company

1. One equation for each relevant restriction; thus three are needed. One slack variable for each restriction, therefore

three of these are required. The two real variables are standard and deluxe products.

2. Complete equations:

$$2.0\,S + 3.0\,D + 1\,M + 0\,W + 0\,P = 24{,}000$$
$$4.0\,S + 3.0\,D + 0\,M + 1\,W + 0\,P = 36{,}000$$
$$0\,S + 1.0\,D + 0\,M + 0\,W + 1\,P = 6{,}000.$$

3. Objective function:

$$(\text{max.})\ \text{T.C.} = (\$1)S + (\$3)D + (\$0)M + (\$0)W + (\$0)P.$$

4. Table of equations:

Contribution	$1	$3	$0	$0	$0	
	S	D	M	W	P	Capacity
Machine	2	3	1	0	0	24,000
Warehouse	4	3	0	1	0	36,000
Paint	0	1	0	0	1	6,000

TROUBLE? Reread Section 4.2 (p. 48).
ANSWERS OK? Proceed to Section 4.3 (p. 56).

Answers 5 and 6: The Zeus Company

5. Initial (origin) solution:

		$1	$3	$0	$0	$0	
		S	D	M	W	P	Production
$0	M	2	3	1	0	0	24,000
$0	W	4	3	0	1	0	36,000
$0	P	0	1	0	0	1	6,000

6. Only slack variables (M, W, P) are in solution at the origin. Their coefficients are always zero and one because, by definition, their "recipes" call only for the resource they represent.

TROUBLE? Reread Section 4.3 (p. 56).
ANSWERS OK? Proceed to Section 4.4 (p. 58).

Answers 7 and 8: The Zeus Company

7. Net effect per unit criterion:

		Standard		Deluxe
Gross gain		$1.00		$3.00
Less:	2 × 0		3 × 0	
	4 × 0		3 × 0	
	0 × 0		1 × 0	
		0.00		0.00
Net per unit		$1.00		$3.00

Select deluxe units for introduction in next stage.

8. Net total effect criterion:

   a) Compute net per unit as in 7.

   b) Now compute number of units which can be introduced:

	If S:		*If D:*
M	24,000 ÷ 2 = 12,000		24,000 ÷ 3 = 8,000
W	36,000 ÷ 4 = 9,000		36,000 ÷ 3 = 12,000
	(limit)		
P	6,000 ÷ 0 = infinity		6,000 ÷ 1 = 6,000
			(limit)

   c) Net total effect computation:

   $$S = 9,000 \times \$1 = \$9,000, \quad D = 6,000 \times \$3 = \$18,000.$$

   Select deluxe units for introduction. Paint slack will be replaced.

   TROUBLE? Reread Section 4.4 (p. 58).
   ANSWERS OK? Proceed to Section 4.5 (p. 63).

Answers 9 to 12: The Zeus Company

9. The 6,000 deluxe units will replace paint slack (*P*). Other variables in the second stage will include *W* (36,000 − 6,000 × 3 = 18,000) and *M* (24,000 − 6,000 × 3 = 6,000).

10. Second stage solution:

		$1	$3	$0	$0	$0	
		S	D	M	W	P	Production
$0	M 2	2	0	1	0	−3	6,000
$0	W 4	4	0	0	1	−3	18,000
$3	D 0	0	1	0	0	1	6,000

11. Value of objective function at second stage:

T.C. = 0 × $1 + 6,000 × $3 + 18,000 × $0 + 6,000 × 0 + 6,000 × $0 = $18,000.

12. Meaning of column coefficients:

a) If standards are introduced, 2 *M*'s, 4 *W*'s, and zero *O*'s will be displaced.

b) If paint slack is re-introduced, 3 *M*'s and 3 *W*'s will be returned to the product mix. One *D* unit would be displaced.

c) Since deluxe units are already in solution, the coefficients are zero and one (as are those for *D* and *M*).

TROUBLE? Reread Section 4.5 (p. 63).

ANSWERS OK? Proceed to Section 4.6 (p. 68).

Answers *13* to *16:* The Zeus Company

13. Variable to be introduced in second stage:

a) Variables currently in solutions (*M*, *W*, *D*) all test zero.

b) Variables not in solution:

		S		P
Gross gain		$1.00		$0.00
Less:	2 × $0		−3 × $0	
	4 × $0		−3 × $0	
	0 × $3		1 × $3	
		0.00		3.00
Net per unit		$1.00		−$3.00

c) Number of *S* units to be introduced:

	S	Production
M	2	6,000/2 = 3,000 (limit)
W	4	18,000/4 = 4,500
D	0	6,000/0 = infinity

14. 3,000 S units will displace M (machining slack) in the next stage. Other variables in solution as follows:

	Production (2nd)	For 3000 S	Production (3rd)
M	6,000	3,000 × 2 = 6,000	out
W	18,000	3,000 × 4 = 12,000	6,000
D	6,000	3,000 × 0 = 0	6,000

15. Third-stage solution table:

   a) Production data from 14.

   b) New coefficients computed as follows:

$$S = 2 \ M + 4 \ W + 0 \ D \ \text{(solve for } M\text{)}$$
$$M = 0.5 \ S - 2 \ W - 0 \ D \ \text{(new } M \text{ coefficients)}$$

   By substitution:

$$P = -3(0.5 \ S - 2 \ W - 0 \ D) - 3 \ W + 1 \ D$$
$$= -1.5 \ S + 3 \ W + 1 \ D \ \text{(new } P \text{ coefficients)}$$

   Coefficients for variables in solution (S, W, D) should be zero and one.

   c) The third-stage table:

		$1	$3	$0	$0	$0	
		S	D	M	W	P	Production
$1	S	1	0	0.5	0	−1.5	3,000
$0	W	0	0	−2	1	3	6,000
$3	D	0	1	0	0	1	6,000

16. Test of third-stage variables:

	S	D	M	W	P
Gross:	$1.00	$3.00	$0.00	$0.00	$0.00
Less:	1.00	3.00	0.50	0.00	1.50
Net	$0.00	$0.00	−$0.50	$0.00	−$1.50

No favorable variables; an optimal solution.

TROUBLE? Reread Section 4.6 (p. 68).

ANSWERS OK? Proceed to Section 4.7 (p. 73).

CHAPTER 5—THE TRANSPORTATION METHOD

Answers *1* to *3:* Uni-Product Company

1. Total plant capacity is 230 while warehouse demand is only 220 carloads. Therefore, a slack warehouse with a requirement of 10 carloads will be required.

2. See Table 5.18.

TABLE 5.18

Whse.	*Plants* 1	2	3	4	*Requirements*
A	8	5	4	6	65
B	8	6	7	5	40
C	10	7	5	3	60
D	6	5	7	3	55
Slack	0	0	0	0	10
Capacity	45	65	45	75	230

3. The total cost represents the sum of all cell assignments times their cost.

(min.) Total cost $= \Sigma \, Q_{ij} \times C_{ij}$.
TROUBLE? Reread Section 5.2 (p. 84).
ANSWERS OK? Proceed to Section 5.3 (p. 90).

Answers 4 to 9: The Uni-Product Company

4. Used cells for initial solution by North to South Row Rule:

A–2 (20), A–3 (45)
B–4 (40)
C–2 (25), C–4 (35)
D–1 (35), D–2 (20)
S–1 (10)

5. Rim — 1 = 8. Eight used cells, so OK to proceed.

6. Interpretation of initial solution:

Plant 1 ships to D (35). Ten units slack.
Plant 2 ships to A (20), C (25), D (20).
Plant 3 ships to A (45).
Plant 4 ships to B (40), C (35).

7. Total cost = $1,070 by North to South Row Rule.

8. Used cells for initial solution by Northwest Corner rule:

A–1 (45); A–2 (20)
B–2 (40)
C–2 (5), C–3 (45), C–4 (10)
D–4 (55)
S–4 (10)

9. Rim — 1 = 8. Eight used cells, so ready for next step.
TROUBLE? Reread pp. 90–96.
ANSWERS OK? Proceed to Section 5.5 (p. 96).

Answers 10 and 11: The Uni-Product Company

10. Stepping-stone evaluation of unused cells:

Cell	Route	Evaluation
C–1	C–2, D–2, D–1	+$2
S–2	S–1, D–1, D–2	+$1
A–4	A–2, C–2, C–4	+$5
B–2	B–4, C–4, C–2	−$3
A–1	A–2, D–2, D–1	+$2
B–1	B–4, C–4, C–2, D–2, D–1	−$2

11. Other evaluations of unused cells:

B–3	A–3, A–2, C–2, C–4, B–4	−$1
C–3	A–3, A–2, C–2	−$1
D–3	A–3, A–2, D–2	+$3
D–4	C–4, C–2, D–2	+$2
S–3	A–3, A–2, D–2, D–1, S–1	+$2
S–4	C–4, C–2, D–2, D–1, S–1	+$5

TROUBLE? Reread Section 5.5.1 (p. 97).

ANSWERS OK? Proceed to Section 5.5.2 (p. 103).

Answers 12 to 14: The Uni-Product Company

12. MODI coefficients for North to South initial solution:

Set $R_A = 0$, then compute using Equation 5.5.

$$K_2 = C_{A2} - R_A = 5 - 0 = 5$$

$$K_3 = C_{A3} - R_A = 4 - 0 = 4$$

$$R_C = C_{C2} - K_2 = 7 - 5 = 2$$

$$R_D = C_{D2} - K_2 = 5 - 5 = 0$$

$$K_1 = C_{D1} - R_D = 6 - 0 = 6$$

$$R_S = C_{S1} - K_1 = 0 - 6 = -6$$

$$K_4 = C_{C4} - R_C = 3 - 2 = 1$$

$$R_B = C_{B4} - K_4 = 5 - 1 = 4$$

13. MODI evaluation of unused cells:

Cell	Computation—Equation 5.6
A–1	$8 - (\ 0 + 6) = +2$
A–4	$6 - (\ 0 + 1) = +5$
B–1	$8 - (\ 4 + 6) = -2$
B–2	$6 - (\ 4 + 5) = -3$
B–3	$7 - (\ 4 + 4) = -1$
C–1	$10 - (\ 2 + 6) = +2$
C–3	$5 - (\ 2 + 4) = -1$
D–3	$7 - (\ 0 + 4) = +3$
D–4	$3 - (\ 0 + 1) = +2$
S–2	$0 - (-6 + 5) = +1$
S–3	$0 - (-6 + 4) = +2$
S–4	$0 - (-6 + 1) = +5$

TROUBLE? Reread Section 5.5.2 (p. 103).

ANSWERS OK? Proceed to Section 5.6 (p. 107).

Answers *15* to *17:* The Uni-Product Company

15. Cells B–1, B–2, B–3, and C–3 all have favorable (negative in this case) evaluations. Select B–2 for introduction since the —$3 evaluation is the highest net effect per unit.

16. Route for B–2 is: B–4, C–4, C–2. Units will be taken from both B–4 and C–2. The 25 units in cell C–2 limit the number of carloads which can be transferred along the route.

17. Used cells in second stage solution:

A–2 (20), A–3 (45)

B–2 (25), B–4 (15)

C–4 (60)

D–1 (35), D–2 (20)

S–1 (10).

TROUBLE? Reread Section 5.6 (p. 107).

ANSWERS OK? Proceed to Section 5.7 (p. 111).

Answers *18* to *22:* The Uni-Product Company

18. Cell evaluations for second stage:

Cell	Route	MODI	Evaluation
B–3	B–2, A–2, A–3	$7 - (\ 1 + 4)$	$+2$
C–2	C–4, B–4, B–2	$7 - (-1 + 5)$	$+3$
D–4	B–4, B–2, D–2	$3 - (\ 0 + 4)$	-1
A–4	A–2, B–2, B–4	$6 - (\ 0 + 4)$	$+2$
S–3	S–1, D–1, D–2, A–2, A–3	$0 - (-6 + 4)$	$+2$
S–4	S–1, D–1, D–2, B–2, B–4	$0 - (-6 + 4)$	$+2$

19. Evaluation of other unused cells:

A–1 = +2   D–3 = +3

B–1 = +1   S–2 = +1

C–1 = +5

C–3 = +2

20. Select D–4, the only favorable cell. Move 15 units over route B–4, B–2, D–2 (cell B–4 controls).

21. See Table 5.19 for third-stage solution.

TABLE 5.19

Whse.	Plants 1 / 6	Plants 2 / 5	Plants 3 / 4	Plants 4 / 3	Requirements
A 0	8 / +2	5 / 20	4 / 45	6 / +3	65
B 1	8 / +1	6 / 40	7 / +2	5 / +1	40
C 0	10 / +4	7 / +2	5 / +1	3 / 60	60
D 0	6 / 35	5 / 5	7 / +3	3 / 15	55
S −6	0 / 10	0 / +1	0 / +2	0 / +3	10
Capacity	45	65	45	75	230

22. All cells have positive evaluations. Since this is a cost minimization problem, these are not favorable evaluations.

TROUBLE? Reread Section 5.7 (p. 111).

ANSWERS OK? Proceed to Section 5.8 (p. 116).